MATH FIRST

E

- Real-World Math Applications
- Multiple Problem-Solving Approaches
- High-Interest Science Topics
- Math and Science Glossary
- Pretest and Posttest

P.O. Box 1749 • Merrimack, NH 03054-1749

Phone 800-782-7300 • Fax 866-424-4056 • www.optionspublishing.com

MATH FIRST • Level E

TABLE OF CONTENTS

Measurement and Geometry

Statistics, Data, and Probability

Problem Solving and Mathematical Reasoning

Reviewer: Madelaine Gallin
District Math Coordinator, retired
Department of Education, New York City, New York

Editor: Carolyn Thresher

Production Supervisor: Sandy Batista

Cover Design: Alan Lee

Product Development: Kane Publishing Services
Project Manager: Amy Goodale
Writer: Joe Brennan, Ann Petroni-McMullen
Editor: Bruce Paddock

Production: Publicom Inc.

Photo Credits:
Illustrations: Eileen Quimby **13, 17, 19, 23, 25, 31, 35, 37, 41, 43, 47, 55** *t*, **63** *t*, **64, 66, 67, 89, 97, 106** *b*; Rich McMahon/Publicom **65, 66, 71**. All other illustrations by Joan Dakai.

Photographs: 13 Frans Lanting/Minden Pictures; **19** Charles E. Mohr/Photo Researchers, Inc.; **25** Tim Davis/Photo Researchers, Inc.; **29** *t* Tom Ulrich/Visuals Unlimited; **29** *b* Joe McDonald/Corbis; **31** Stuart Westmoreland/Corbis; **35** Beverly Joubert/NGS Image Collection; **37** PhotoDisc/GettyImages; **41** Prance/Visuals Unlimited; **49** Bill Howe/Photri/Microstock; **53** John Gerlach/Visuals Unlimited; **55** PhotoDisc/GettyImages; **59** Kitchin & V Hurst/NHPA; **61** *t* Joseph Sohm/Visions of America/Corbis; **61** *b* Joseph Sohm/ChromoSohm Inc./Corbis; **62** Joseph Sohm/ChromoSohm Inc./Corbis; **63** PhotoDisc/GettyImages; **73** Royalty-Free/Corbis; **77** Bettmann/Corbis; **79** PhotoDisc/GettyImages; **83** *t* PhotoDisc/GettyImages; **83** *b* Bruce Dale/NGS Image Collection; **85** Royalty-Free/Corbis; **91** Popperfoto/Alamy Limited; **95** PhotoDisc/GettyImages; **97** Annie Griffiths Belt/Corbis; **101** Ric Ergenbright/Corbis.

ISBN 1-59137-111-2
Options Publishing Inc.
P.O. Box 1749
Merrimack, NH 03054-1749
TOLL FREE: 800-782-7300 FAX: 866-424-4056
www.optionspublishing.com

15 14 13 12 11 10 9 8 7 6 5 4 3

PRETEST

Fill in the circle next to the correct answer.

For short response questions, write the answer in the space provided.

1. Elsie was asked to compare the decimals.
She had to write >, <, or =. What should she write?

0.65 ☐ **0.47**

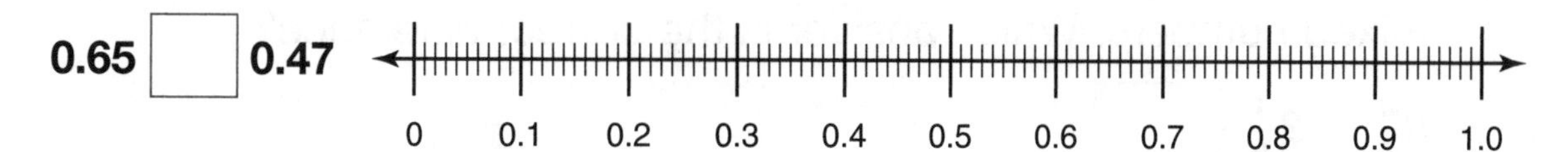

2. Greg wants to compare the decimals. Which symbol should he use?

0.32 ☐ **0.59**

Ⓐ >　　Ⓑ <　　Ⓒ =

3. Show Jose how to add fractions.

$\frac{2}{8} + \frac{3}{8} =$ ☐

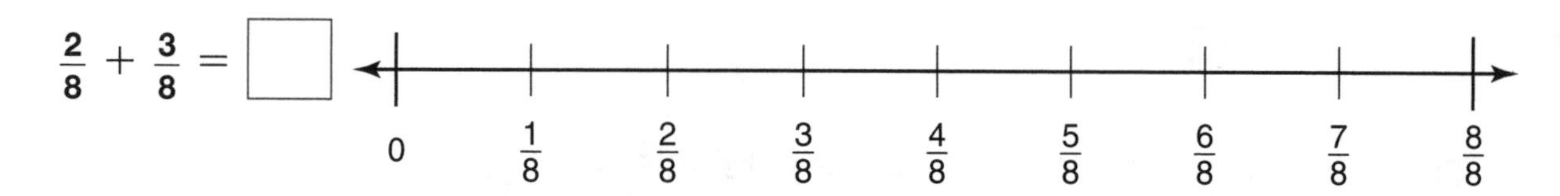

4. Sara has to subtract the fractions. Help her choose the correct answer.

$\frac{4}{5} - \frac{2}{5} =$ ☐

Ⓐ $\frac{5}{5}$　　Ⓑ $\frac{3}{5}$　　Ⓒ $\frac{2}{5}$　　Ⓓ $\frac{1}{5}$

5 Help Jenny add the mixed numbers.

$3\frac{2}{7} + 1\frac{4}{7} = \square$

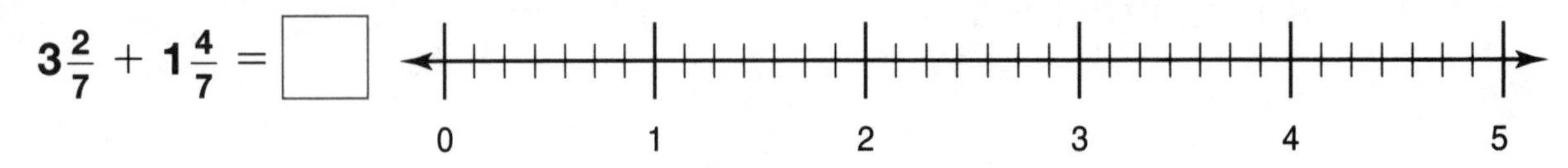

6 Alex was asked to find the difference between these mixed numbers. Which answer is the correct difference?

$6\frac{4}{5} - 2\frac{1}{5} = \square$

Ⓐ $8\frac{3}{5}$ Ⓑ $4\frac{1}{3}$ Ⓒ $4\frac{1}{5}$ Ⓓ $4\frac{3}{5}$

7 Use the grid to help you write the equivalent fraction for a percent for Laura.

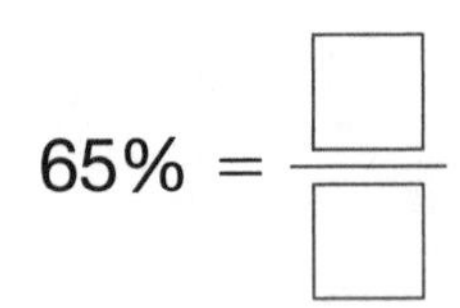

$65\% = \frac{\square}{\square}$

8 Leon asked which percent is equivalent to $\frac{3}{4}$.
What would you tell him?

Ⓐ 75% Ⓑ 55% Ⓒ 34% Ⓓ 30%

9 Barbara said that she knows how to multiply 6×43 using the Distributive Property. Show how Barbara solves this problem.

$6 \times 43 =$

10 Ryan knows how to use the Associative Property to multiply. What is Ryan's answer?

$(8 \times 5) \times 9$

Ⓐ 40 Ⓑ 45 Ⓒ 350 Ⓓ 360

11 Use the counters to solve.

$3 + 12 + x = 23$

12 Use algebra to solve.

$y \times 5 = 45$

Ⓐ $y = 5$ Ⓑ $y = 9$ Ⓒ $y = 40$ Ⓓ $y = 50$

13 Find the perimeter and area of the board.

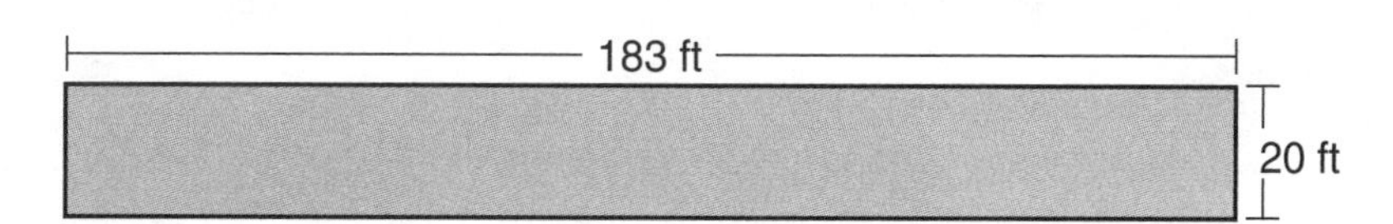

Perimeter = ☐ + ☐ + ☐ + ☐ = ☐ **ft**

Area = ☐ × ☐ = ☐ **sq ft**

14 Find the perimeter and the area.

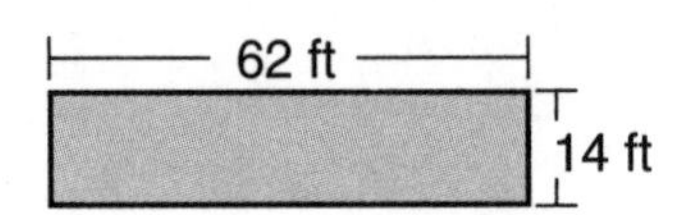

$P = 2(\ell + w) = 2(\square + \square) = 2(\square) = \square$ **ft**

$A = \ell \times w = \square \times \square = \square$ **sq ft**

15 On the coordinate grid, draw the points of these coordinate pairs. Label each point.

Point A (2, 3)

Point B (2, 5)

Point C (4, 5)

Point D (4, 3)

Connect the points in order. What are the coordinates of the point in the center of the figure you drew? ________________

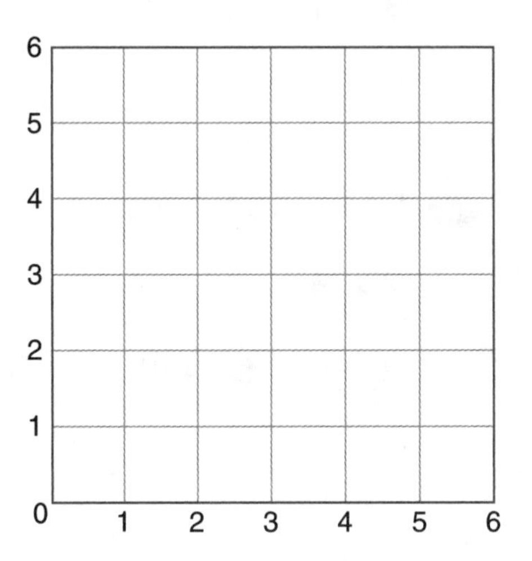

16 Use the scale drawing and a centimeter ruler to answer the question.

How tall are the actual Upper Falls of the Yellowstone River?

________________ **m**

Upper Falls of the Yellowstone River
Scale: 1 cm = 6 m

17 Use the circle graph to answer the question.

Which sport is represented by about $\frac{1}{4}$ of the graph?

____

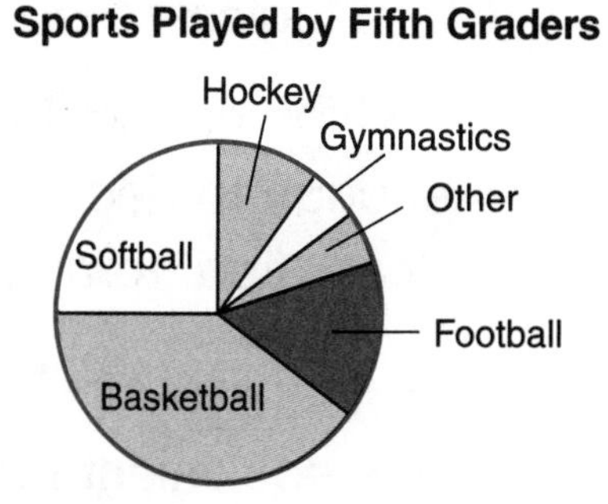

18 Use the bar graph to answer the question.

Which two categories use about the same amount of water as is used for Watering Plants?

Ⓐ Leaky Faucets and Toilets

Ⓑ Toilets and Showering

Ⓒ Leaky Faucets and Showering

Ⓓ Leaky Faucets and Washing

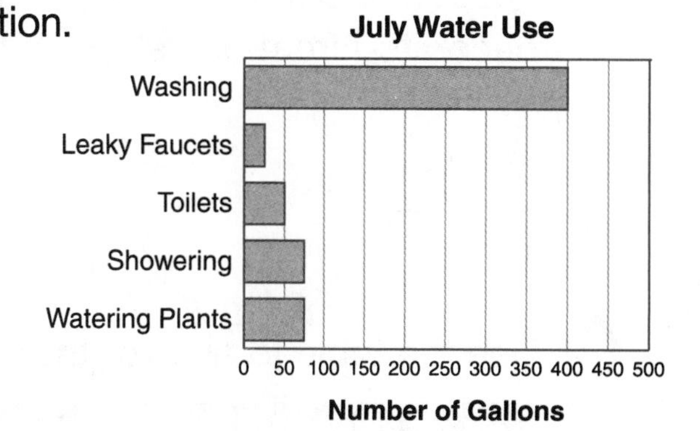

19 Use the line graph to answer the question.

Between which ten-year period was there the greatest change in population?

____

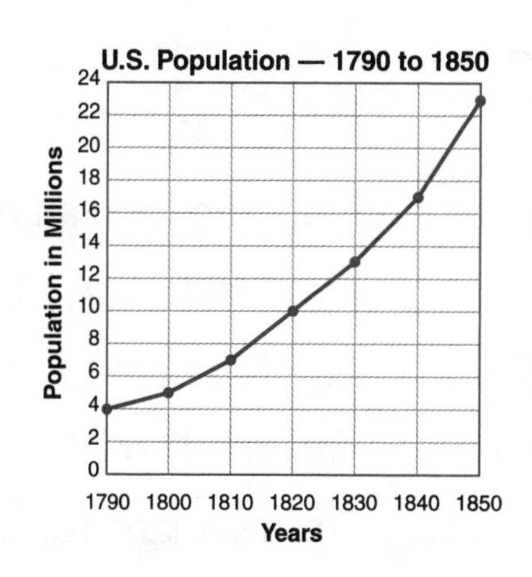

20 Use logical reasoning to solve the problem.

A shipment contains 120 shells. Each group of 20 shells is enough to decorate 1 mirror. How many mirrors could be decorated from one shipment of shells?

_____ mirrors could be decorated with 120 shells.

21 Use equivalent fractions to solve the problem.

A shipment contains 600 shells. Each group of 30 shells is enough to decorate 1 mirror. How many mirrors could be decorated from one shipment of shells?

$$\frac{1}{30} = \frac{x}{600}$$

$x = \square$

22 Use the table to answer the question.

Summer Reading	
Name	**Number of Books Read**
Nora	13
Dave	11
Cris	13
Juan	7
Rosa	10

What are the median and the mode of the data?

Ⓐ Median: 7, Mode: 11

Ⓑ Median: 11, Mode: 13

Ⓒ Median: 13, Mode: 11

Ⓓ Median: 13, Mode: 13

23 Solve by making a list.

A male and a female llama produced 2 offspring. One of their offspring was female and she had 3 babies in her life. One of her babies was a male. How many males and females were in this family, counting the parents?

There were ____ males and ____ females in this family.

24 Solve by using a chart.

Eric's dogs always had one more male than female in their litter. The first litter had 2 females. The next litter had 3 females. The third litter had 2 females. How many puppies were in the 3 litters in all?

	Females (F)	Males (F + 1)	Total
Litter 1			
Litter 2			
Litter 3			

___ + ___ + ___ = ___

There were ____ puppies in all.

25 Solve using a table.

On the first day of a fossil dig, 6 students were digging at Site A. Three more students than this were at Site B.

On Day 2, the number of students at Site A was increased by 2 and the number at Site B was tripled from the day before.

On the last day, the number of students at Site A was the same as the number the first day. The number of students at Site B was 1 less than at Site A that day. How many students in all worked at each site during the three days?

	Day 1	Day 2	Day 3	Total
Site A				
Site B				

The total number of students who worked at Site A was ____.

The total number of students who worked at Site B was ____.

26 Solve using logic.

The first day of an excavation, scientists digging for fossils found twice as many fossils at Site A as at Site B. They found 6 fossils at Site B. On the second day, they found 2 more fossils at each site than they found the day before. How many fossils did they find at each site in all?

Scientists found ____ fossils at Site A in all.

Scientists found ____ fossils at Site B in all.

LESSON 1

Compare Decimals

Teeny Tiny Mammals Have you ever seen a shrew? Shrews are tiny mouselike animals that burrow in the ground. They are also among the smallest animals in the world. One kind, the Savi's pygmy shrew, has an average weight of 0.07 ounce. That's about the weight of two paper clips! The common tree shrew weighs about 0.3 ounce. At 0.89 ounce, a wood mouse almost seems like a monster!

Each day, a pygmy shrew eats more than its own weight in food. Some shrews have poisonous spit to stun their prey. Other shrews have a gland that gives off a horrible smell to keep other animals from eating them.

Common Tree Shrew

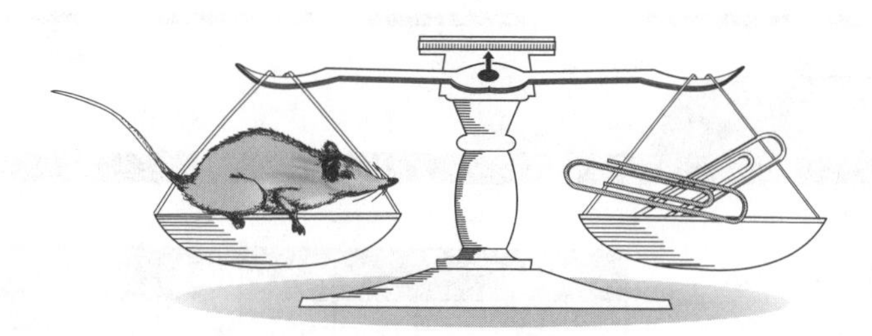

Give It a Try

The weights of a pygmy shrew and a common tree shrew are given as decimals. Neither animal weighs a full ounce.

If a pygmy shrew weighs 0.07 ounce and a common tree shrew weighs 0.3 ounce, which one weighs more?

Compare.
Use >, <, or =.

> **> means "is greater than"**
> **< means "is less than"**
> **= means "is equal to"**

0.07 ☐ **0.3**

- You can use a number line to determine which weight is larger.
- Or, you can use place value to compare the two weights. Before you do, add zeroes to make sure each decimal has the same number of digits to the right of the decimal point.

Approach 1: Use a Number Line

STEP 1 Use a number line from 0.0 through 0.5. Find each decimal on the number line.

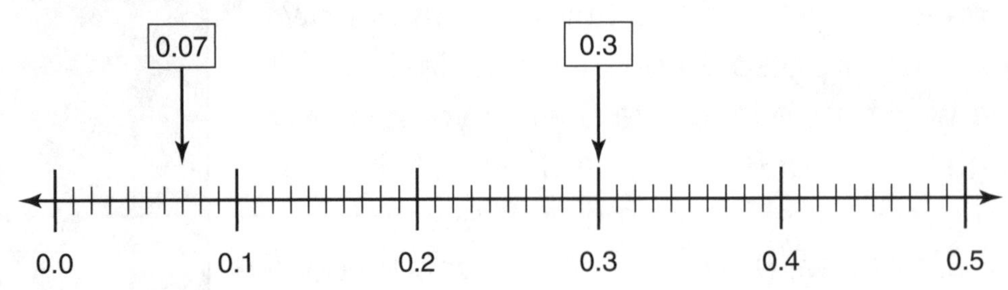

STEP 2 Compare the decimals to find which is greater.

The number farther to the right on the number line is greater. 0.3 is to the right of 0.07, so 0.3 is greater than 0.07.

Write >, <, or = in the box. **0.3** ☐ **0.07**

Approach 2: Use Place Value

STEP 1 Write one decimal below the other. Make sure to line up the decimal points.

STEP 2 Compare digits in each place, starting from the left.

Ones	.	Tenths	Hundredths
0	.	0	7
0	.	3	0

The digits are the same. Compare the tenths.

The digits are different, so compare them to find which is greater.

Write >, <, or = in the box.

Since 0 < 3 then

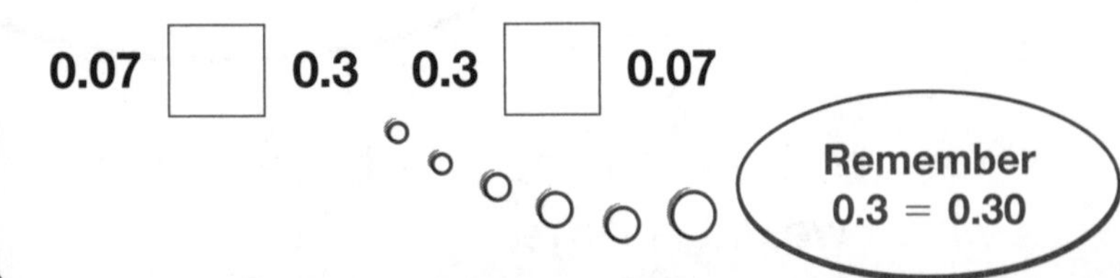

If a pygmy shrew weighs 0.07 ounce and a common tree shrew weighs 0.3 ounce, which one weighs more?

A ______________ weighs more than a ______________ because ____ ☐ ____.

Practice This

Mark each decimal on the number line. Then compare the decimals. Write >, <, or =.

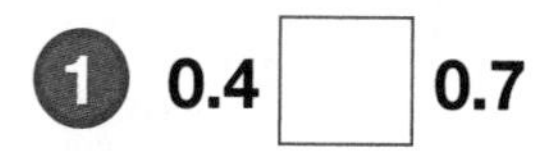

1. 0.4 ☐ 0.7

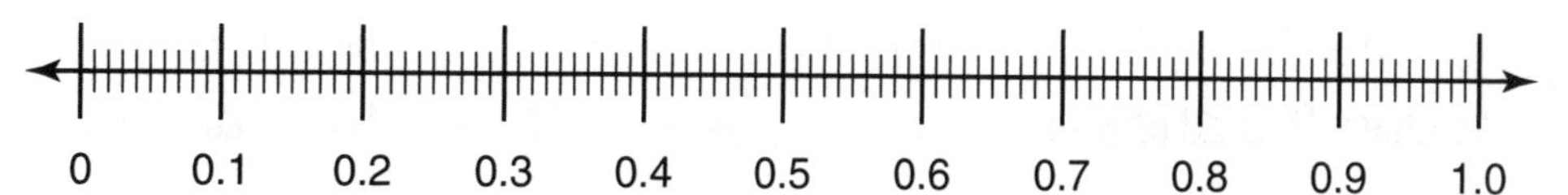

2. 0.31 ☐ 0.27

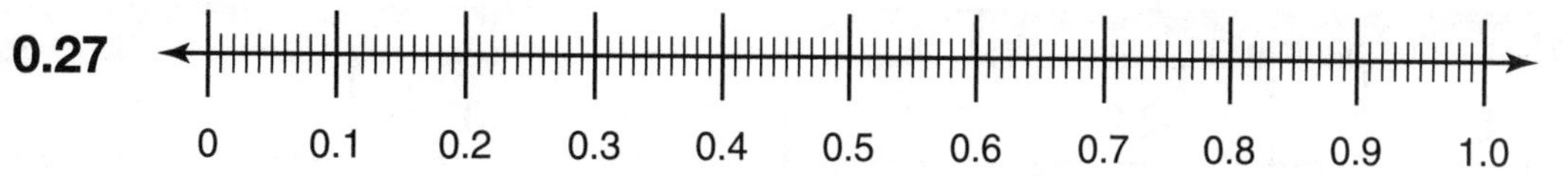

3. 0.6 ☐ 0.01

Use place value to compare the decimals. Write >, <, or =.

4. 0.20 ☐ 0.21

Ones	.	Tenths	Hundredths
0	.	2	0
0	.	2	1

5. 0.44 ☐ 0.34

Ones	.	Tenths	Hundredths
0	.	4	4
0	.	3	4

6. 0.07 ☐ 0.12

Ones	.	Tenths	Hundredths
0	.	0	7
0	.	1	2

7. 2.29 ☐ 2.25

8. 0.49 ☐ 0.57

9. 1.85 ☐ 1.85

10. 9.1 ☐ 9.08

11. 6.9 ☐ 7.01

12. 0.81 ☐ 0.18

13. 0.3 ☐ 0.30

14. 4.51 ☐ 4.53

15. 0.05 ☐ 0.40

Practice This

Compare the decimals.

16 Write which decimal is the greatest. Explain how you found the answer.

0.27 **0.23** **0.21**

Ones	.	Tenths	Hundredths
0	.	2	7
0	.	2	3
0	.	2	1

____

____

____

17 Write which decimal is the least. Explain how you found the answer.

0.71 **0.76** **0.67**

Ones	.	Tenths	Hundredths
0	.	7	1
0	.	7	6
0	.	6	7

____

____

____

18 Choose the smallest decimal from the circle. Write that decimal in the bottom rung of the ladder. Choose a larger decimal from the box and write it in the next rung. Without erasing, how far up the ladder can you get before you run out of decimals?

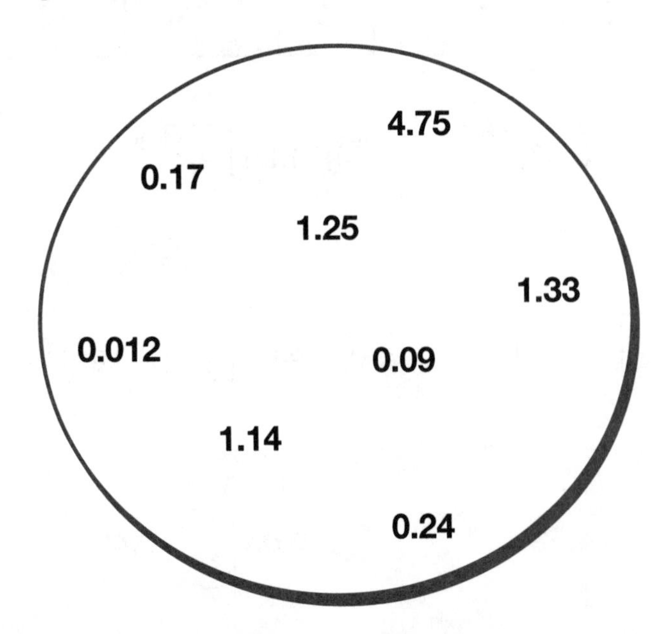

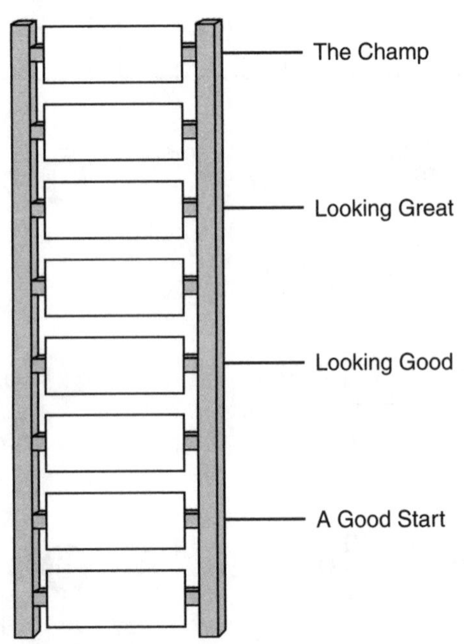

Problem Solving

Bumblebee Bat, Actual Size

The smallest mammal on the planet is the bumblebee bat. The bumblebee bat weighs about 0.07 ounce, but it is considered smaller than the pygmy shrew because its body is shorter. The bumblebee bat's long, broad wings allow it to float in one place above the treetops and pick off spiders to eat.

Pygmy Shrew, Actual Size

Solve.

1 Scientists measure animals' body parts to compare them. Dr. Mustafa measured the hind foot of a pygmy shrew to be 5.7 mm long. The hind foot of a bumblebee bat was 5.9 mm long.

Which animal has the larger hind foot?

a. Write what you know.

pygmy shrew's hind foot: ______ mm long

bumblebee bat's hind foot: ______ mm long

b. You can use > and < to compare the numbers.

______ > ______ or ______ < ______

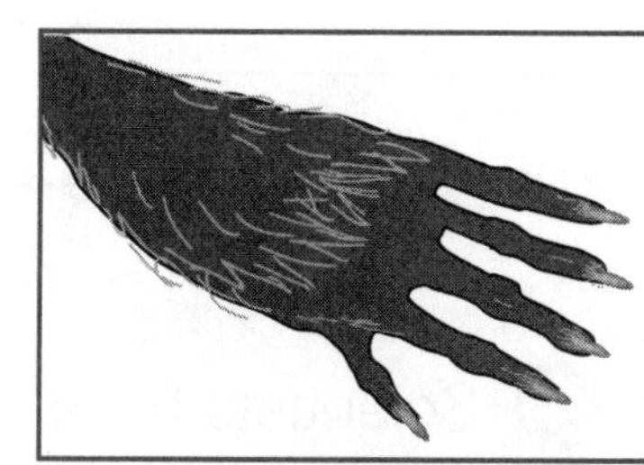
Hind Foot of Bumblebee Bat

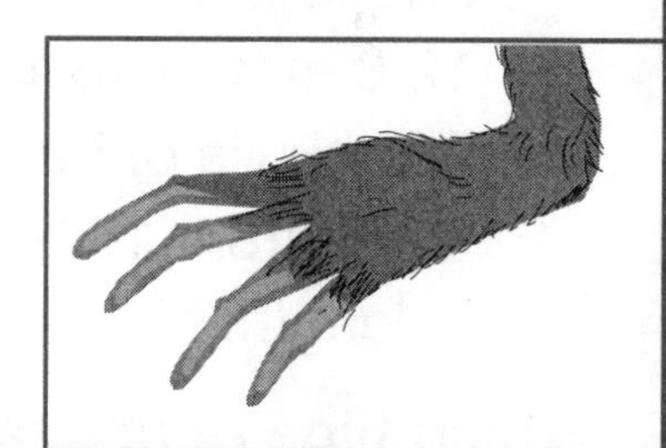
Hind Foot of Pygmy Shrew

Answer:

Dr. Mustafa found that the hind foot of the ____________ is larger than the hind foot of the ____________.

Problem Solving Practice

2 A harvest mouse, running through the fields in England, weighs 0.21 oz. A Western harvest mouse in Canada weighs 0.39 oz.

Which mouse is heavier?

What do you know?

____

____

____

____

____

The ______________ is heavier.

3 A pygmy shrew can eat 0.14 oz of insects every day. The shrew weighs about 0.07 oz. A Western harvest mouse eats about 0.06 oz of oats in a day. It weighs about 0.39 oz.

Which animal eats more than its own weight in food each day?

What do you know?

____

____

____

The ______________ eats more than its own weight in food each day.

4 Scientists have measured the skulls of different pygmy shrews and found that they range from 12.0 mm to 13.1 mm in length. The skulls of bumblebee bats range from 10.3 mm to 11.5 mm in length.

Which type of animal might have a skull measurement of 12.73 mm?

____

Explain your answer.

____

____

____

____

5 A common tree shrew is 13.5 cm from head to tail. A Savi's pygmy shrew measures 6.3 cm, and a common wood mouse is 14.5 cm long.

Which of these animals is longest?

____

Explain your answer.

____

____

____

____

____

____

LESSON 2

Add and Subtract Fractions with Like Denominators

Ozark Blind Cave Salamander

Mammoth Cave Animals Mammoth Cave in Kentucky is the largest cave system in the world. How large is it? Geologists think there may be 600 miles of caves and passageways that haven't even been discovered yet!

Over 130 species of animals live in Mammoth Cave. They can be divided into three groups: Troglobites (TROG•lu•bytes) are animals that live their entire lives in caves. Troglophiles (TROG•lu•files) are animals that live part of their lives in caves. Trogloxenes (TROG•lu•zenes) are animals that find shelter in caves.

About $\frac{2}{3}$ of the species in Mammoth Cave are troglophiles or trogloxenes. Only $\frac{1}{3}$ are troglobites and spend their entire lives in the caves. These include fish, shrimp, crayfish, millipedes, and various insects. Because there is no light deep in the cave, most of these troglobites are completely blind. Some of them don't even have eyes!

Give It a Try

The number of species that are troglobites and the number that are troglophiles or trogloxenes are expressed as fractions of a whole.

Find the sum $\frac{1}{3} + \frac{2}{3}$ and the difference $\frac{2}{3} - \frac{1}{3}$.

Find the sum and the difference.

$\frac{1}{3} + \frac{2}{3} = \square$

$\frac{2}{3} - \frac{1}{3} = \square$

- You can use a number line to add and subtract the fractions.
- Or, you can draw models to help you add and subtract.

Approach 1: Use a Number Line

STEP 1 To add, find the first fraction on the number line.

STEP 2 Then move to the right a distance equal to the second fraction.

As you move on the number line, you can count one third, two thirds, three thirds, and so on.

$\frac{1}{3} + \frac{2}{3} = \square$

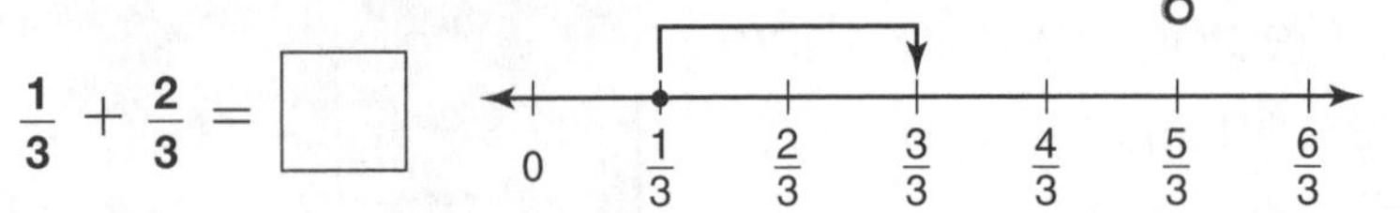

STEP 1 To subtract, find the first fraction on the number line.

STEP 2 Then move to the left a distance equal to the second fraction.

$\frac{2}{3} - \frac{1}{3} = \square$

0 $\frac{1}{3}$ $\frac{2}{3}$ $\frac{3}{3}$ $\frac{4}{3}$ $\frac{5}{3}$ $\frac{6}{3}$

Approach 2: Draw Models

Make sure the boxes you draw are all equal in size.

STEP 1 For each fraction, draw a number of boxes equal to the denominator. Shade a number of boxes equal to each numerator, as seen on the right.

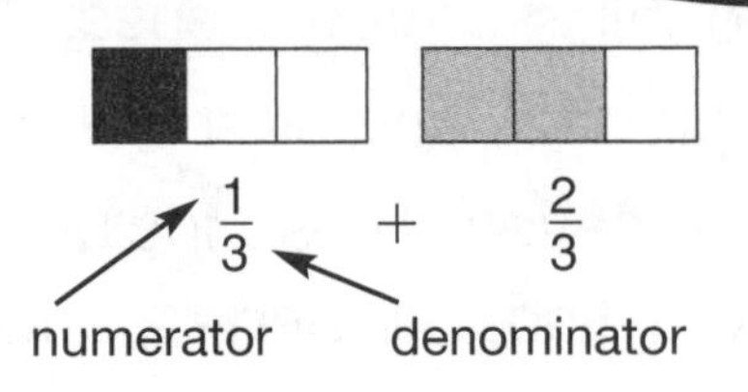

STEP 2 To add, draw a third set of boxes for the sum. Count the shaded boxes in the first two sets. Then shade the same number of boxes in the third set.

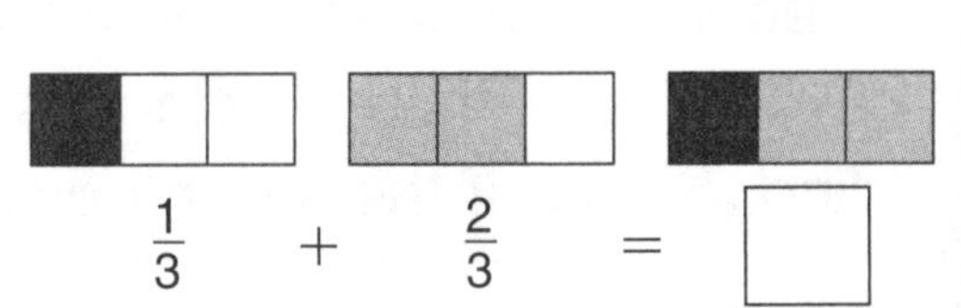

STEP 1 For the first fraction, draw a number of boxes equal to the denominator. Using a pencil, shade the number of boxes equal to the numerator.

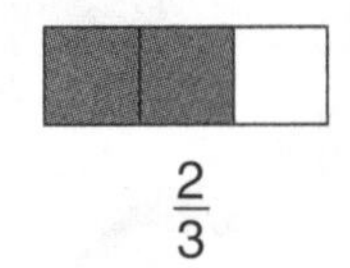

STEP 2 To subtract, find the numerator of the second fraction. Erase the shading from that number of boxes.

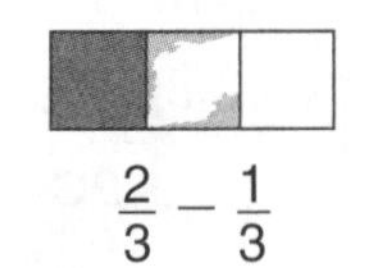

$\frac{1}{3} + \frac{2}{3} = \square$ $\frac{2}{3} - \frac{1}{3} = \square$

Practice This

Use the number lines to show how the fractions can be added or subtracted.

1 $\frac{3}{8} + \frac{4}{8} = \square$

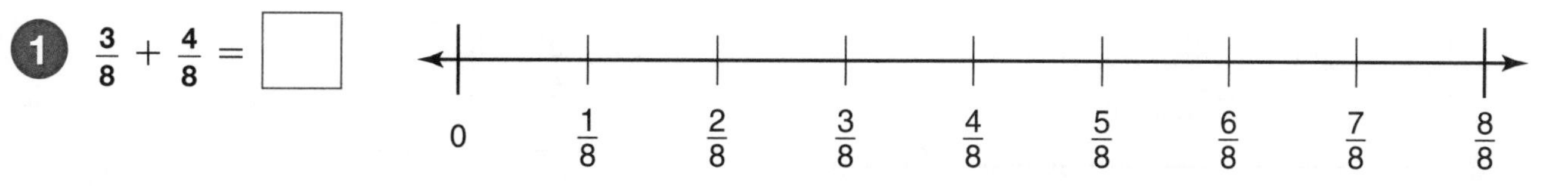

2 $\frac{3}{6} + \frac{2}{6} = \square$

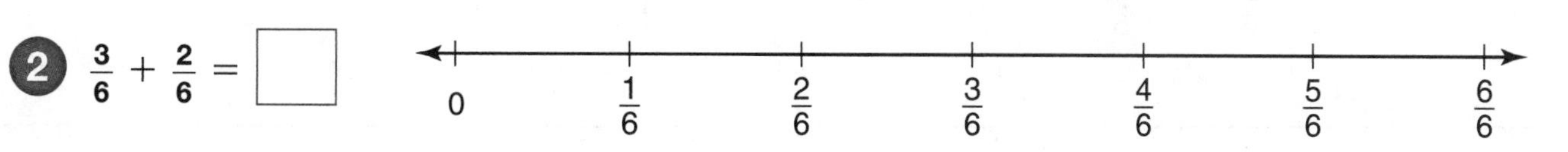

3 $\frac{4}{7} - \frac{3}{7} = \square$

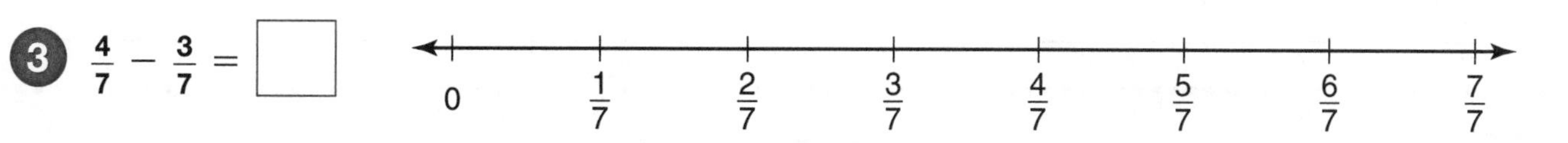

Use the models to add or subtract the fractions.

4 $\frac{2}{4} + \frac{1}{4} = \square$

+ =

5 $\frac{3}{5} - \frac{2}{5} = \square$

6 $\frac{1}{5} + \frac{3}{5} = \square$

7 $\frac{4}{9} + \frac{3}{9} = \square$

8 $\frac{6}{8} - \frac{5}{8} = \square$

9 $\frac{1}{2} - \frac{1}{2} = \square$

Practice This

10 Write the sum. Explain how you found the answer.

$\frac{1}{5} + \frac{3}{5} = \square$

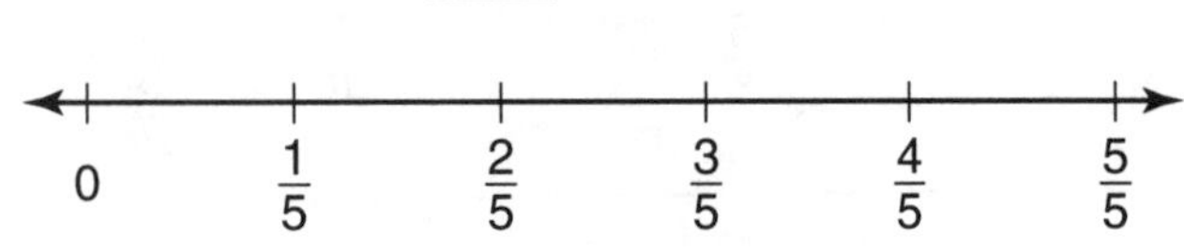

11 Write the difference. Explain how you found the answer.

$\frac{5}{6} - \frac{2}{6} = \square$

12 Start with a fraction in Column 1. Find the fraction in Column 2 that has the same denominator. Perform the operation indicated between the columns, and write the answer in Column 3. Repeat for Columns 4 through 6.

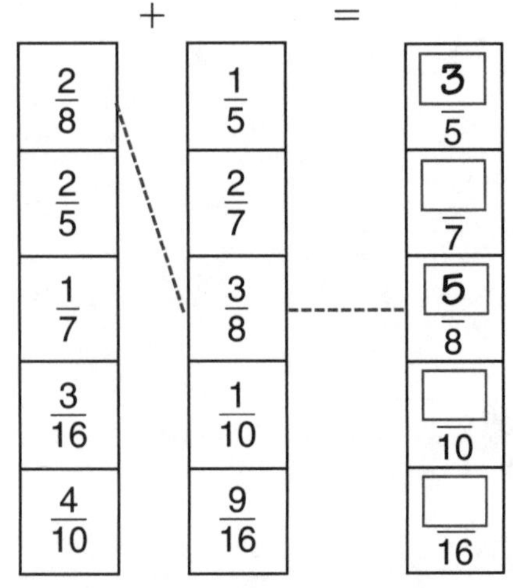

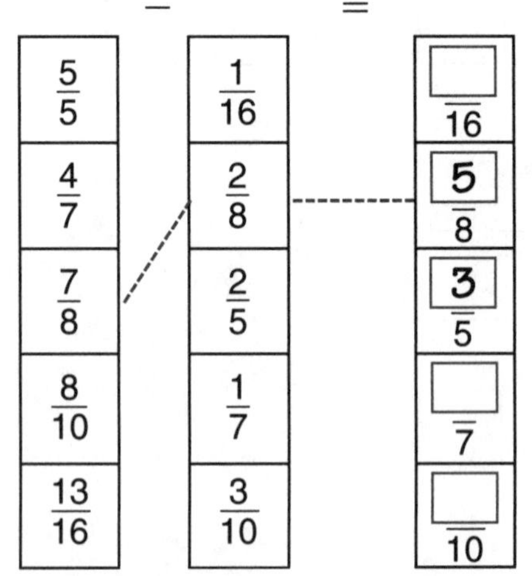

Problem Solving

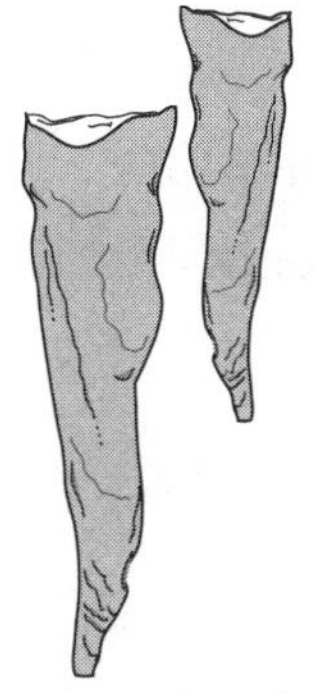

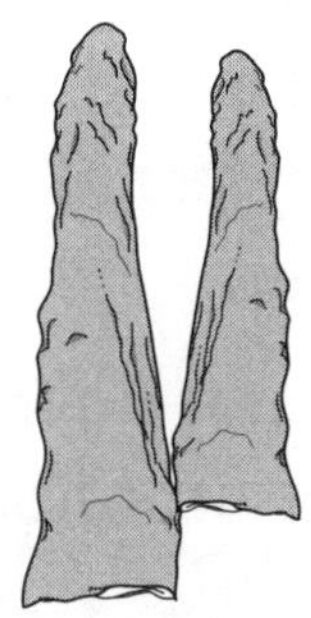

Stalactites Stalagmites Gypsum Flowers

In a cave, dripping water can leave dissolved minerals behind. Over time, the minerals build up and become beautiful formations.

Solve.

1 A class from Ella Smalls Middle School took a trip to Elephant Cave. In one chamber they found 11 different formations. Of these, 3 were stalagmites and 6 were stalactites. The rest were gypsum flowers.

Of all the formations in the chamber, what fraction were gypsum flowers?

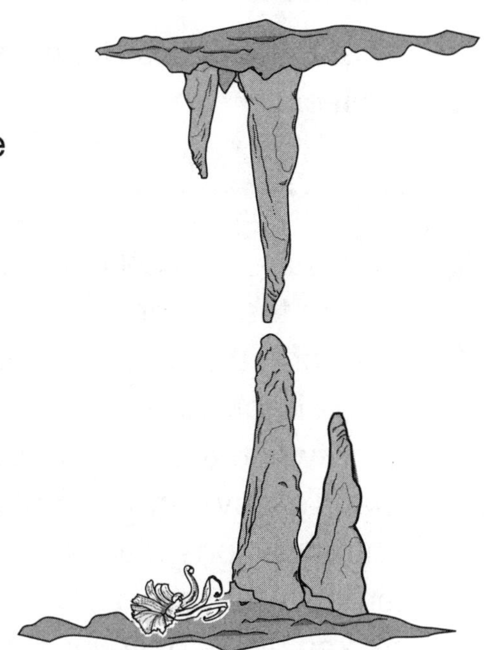

a. Write what you know.

_______ formations in all

_______ stalagmites

_______ stalactites

b. Decide what operation(s) you will use.

_______ + _______ = _______

_______ – _______ = _______

Answer:

__________ of all the formations were gypsum flowers.

Problem Solving Practice

2 Bennie counted the animals he saw by a small cave near his house. He counted 8 bats, 5 crickets, and 2 fish.

What fraction of the animals was insects?

What do you know?

____

____

____

_____ of the animals Bennie saw were insects.

3 Tanya examined 8 gypsum flowers. She found that 6 were reddish in color due to iron in the water. In fact, 3 of the 6 were very dark red.

Of all the gypsum flowers Tanya looked at, what fraction were light red?

What do you know?

____

____

_____ of the gypsum flowers were light red.

4 Caves are divided into three zones: the entrance zone is in the front, the dark zone is deep in the back, and the twilight zone is between the two. A map of Mann's Cave shows that the entrance zone makes up $\frac{1}{14}$ of its length. The cave's dark zone makes up $\frac{9}{14}$ of its length.

What fraction of the cave's length is the twilight zone?

____

Explain your answer.

____

____

____

5 One morning, the temperature inside Vena Cave was 58°F. That evening it was 49°F. The temperature had dropped 2°F due to the change in the water temperature of a river in the cave. The rest of the drop was caused by air movement in the cave.

What fraction of the total drop in temperature did the air movement account for?

____

Explain your answer.

____

____

____

Add and Subtract Mixed Numbers with Like Denominators

The Hard Part Is the Landing How far could you jump if you were a frog? Frogs are good jumpers. The record holder is a South African sharp-nosed frog named Leaping Lena. He (yes, Lena was a "he") covered 32 feet 3 inches in 3 jumps. This may not sound like much, but Lena was only 2 inches long. He jumped almost 200 times his own length. To match that feat, a 6-foot-tall person would have to jump nearly 1,200 feet!

The most famous frog jumping contest may be the one in Calaveras County, California. There, another South African sharp-nosed frog covered about 15 feet in one jump! Why isn't the exact distance recorded? Because, unfortunately, the contest was already over. The frog was trying to avoid being picked up. The jump didn't count!

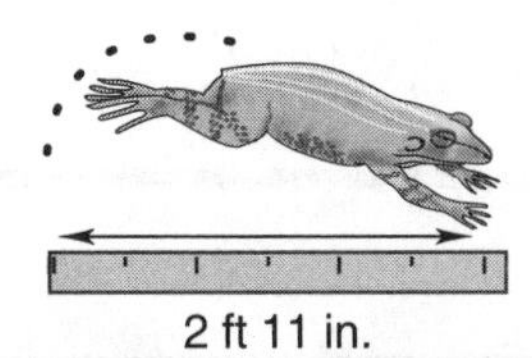

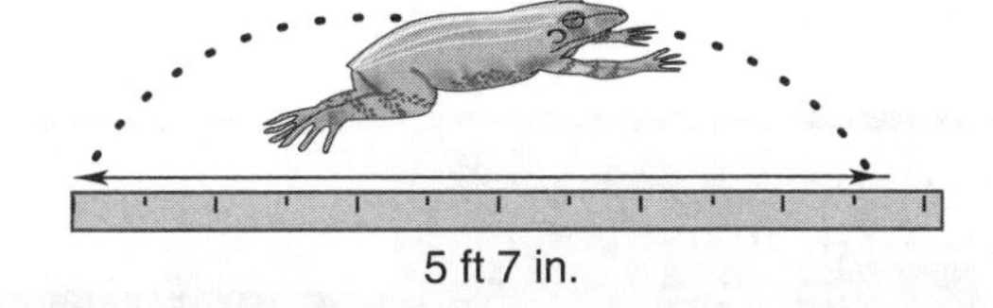

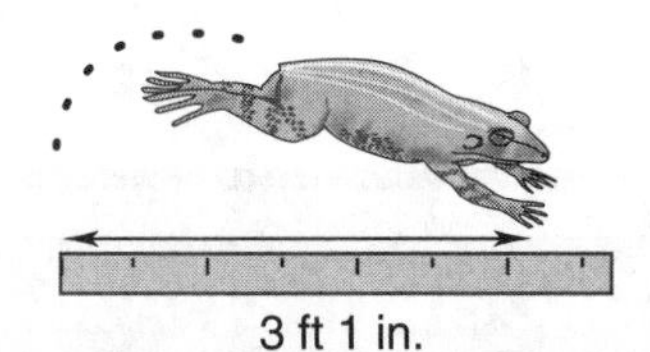

Give It a Try

Each of this frog's jumps can be expressed as a mixed number: $2\frac{11}{12}$ ft, $5\frac{7}{12}$ ft, and $3\frac{1}{12}$ ft.

How far did the frog go in the first two jumps?

How much longer was the second jump than the third one?

Find the sum and difference.

You may end up with an improper fraction in your answer. If you do, be sure to rename it.

$\mathbf{2\frac{11}{12} + 5\frac{7}{12} =}$ ☐

$\mathbf{5\frac{7}{12} - 3\frac{1}{12} =}$ ☐

- You can use a number line to add and subtract mixed numbers.
- Or, you can add or subtract the whole numbers and the fractions separately.

Approach 1: Use a Number Line

STEP 1 To add, find the first mixed number on the number line.

STEP 2 Move to the right a distance equal to the second mixed number.

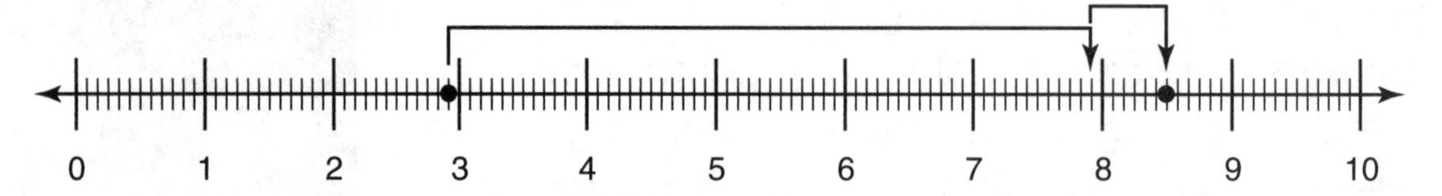

$2\frac{11}{12} + 5\frac{7}{12} = \square$

STEP 1 To subtract, find the first mixed number on the number line.

STEP 2 Move to the left a distance equal to the second mixed number.

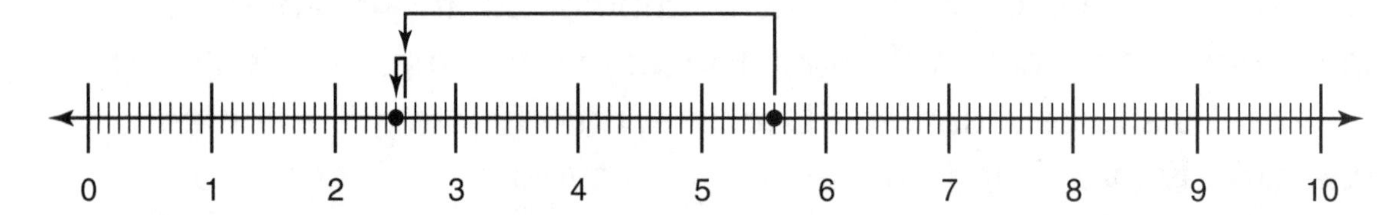

$5\frac{7}{12} - 3\frac{1}{12} = \square$

Approach 2: Add or Subtract Whole Numbers and Fractions Separately

	Add	Subtract
	$2\frac{11}{12} + 5\frac{7}{12}$	$5\frac{7}{12} - 3\frac{1}{12}$
STEP 1 Calculate with the whole numbers.	$2 + 5 = 7$	$5 - 3 = 2$
STEP 2 Calculate with the fractions.	$\frac{11}{12} + \frac{7}{12} = \frac{18}{12} = 1\frac{6}{12}$	$\frac{7}{12} - \frac{1}{12} = \frac{6}{12}$
STEP 3 Simplify the answer.	$7 + 1\frac{6}{12} = \square$	$2 + \frac{6}{12} = \square$

How far did the frog go in the first two jumps? $2\frac{11}{12} + 5\frac{7}{12} = \square$

How much longer was the second jump than the third one? $5\frac{7}{12} - 3\frac{1}{12} = \square$

Practice This

Use the number lines to add or subtract the mixed numbers.

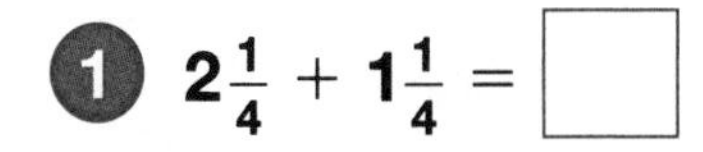

1 $2\frac{1}{4} + 1\frac{1}{4} = \square$

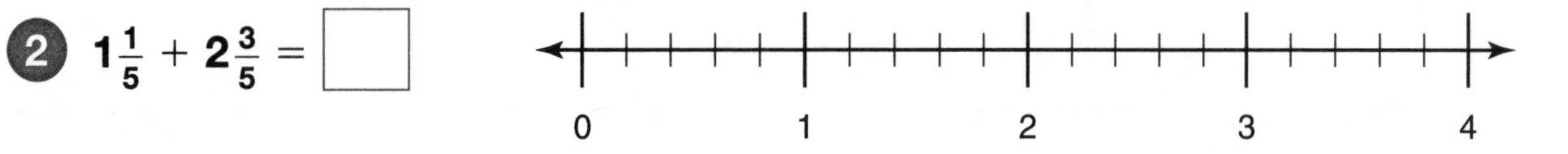

2 $1\frac{1}{5} + 2\frac{3}{5} = \square$

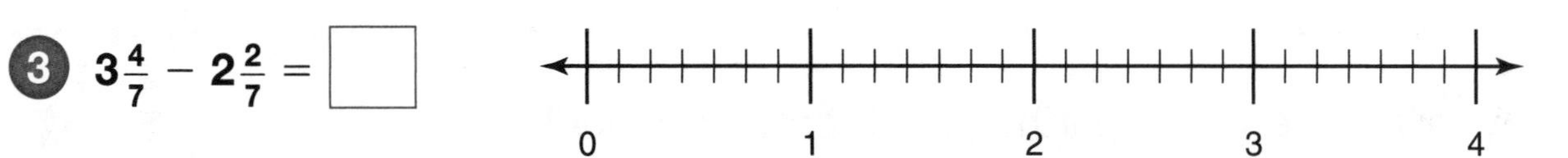

3 $3\frac{4}{7} - 2\frac{2}{7} = \square$

Find each sum or difference by adding or subtracting the whole numbers and the fractions separately.

4 $8\frac{2}{9} + 1\frac{5}{9} = \square$

$8\frac{2}{9} + 1\frac{5}{9} = \square\,\frac{\square}{\square}$

5 $4\frac{5}{6} - 3\frac{1}{6} = \square$

$4\frac{5}{6} - 3\frac{1}{6} = \square\,\frac{\square}{\square}$

6 $7\frac{3}{5} - 2\frac{1}{5} = \square$

7 $12\frac{2}{4} + 4\frac{1}{4} = \square$

8 $9\frac{3}{8} + 5\frac{2}{8} = \square$

9 $2\frac{7}{10} - 1\frac{4}{10} = \square$

Practice This

10 Write the sum. Explain how you found the answer.

$4\frac{3}{8} + 2\frac{3}{8} = \square$

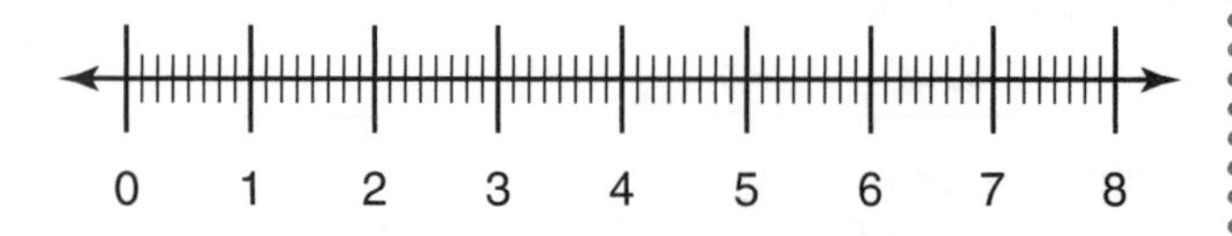

____

____

____

11 Write the difference. Explain how you found the answer.

$5\frac{4}{5} - 3\frac{2}{5} = \square$

$5\frac{4}{5} - 3\frac{2}{5} = \square\,\frac{\square}{\square}$

____

____

____

12 Play this game with a partner. Each partner should pick either the Sums or Differences board. Spin the spinner by using a paper clip and a pencil. Hold down the paper clip on the spinner with the point of the pencil. Spin the spinner.

Then pick a box in that row of your board. Find the mixed numbers both above your box on the horizontal axis and to the left of your box on the vertical axis. Then write the sum or difference of the two numbers in the box you chose.

Check your partner's answers. If your partner must erase an incorrect answer, he or she loses a turn. The first board to have three correct answers in a row wins!

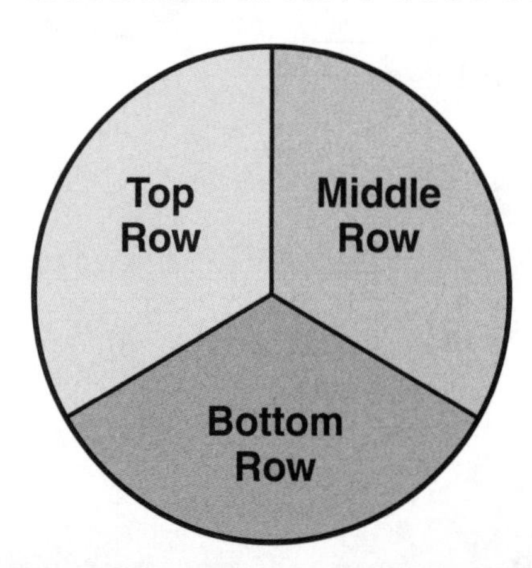

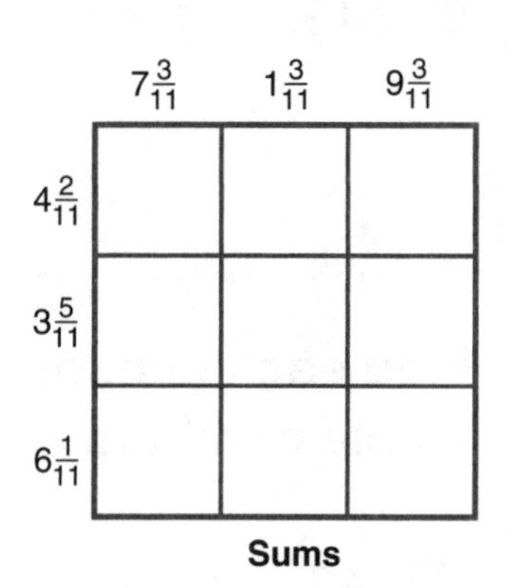

Sums

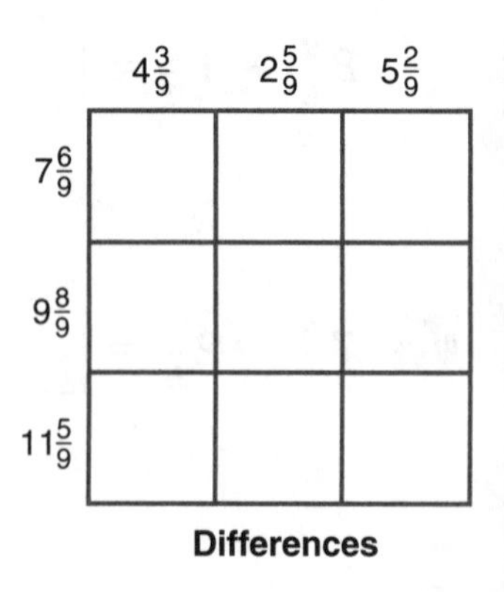

Differences

Problem Solving

Fowler's Toad

A scientist named A. S. Rand once tested the jumping ability of Fowler's toads. On grass, the toads jumped anywhere from 1 ft to 1 ft $10\frac{1}{2}$ in. But on sand, they only jumped from 6 in. to $14\frac{1}{2}$ in.

Solve.

1 Danitra decided to check Rand's findings. First she placed a toad on grass. It made two jumps—one was $19\frac{3}{4}$ in. and one was $13\frac{1}{4}$ in. Then she put the toad in the sand pit at the school track. Again she measured two jumps. The first was $7\frac{1}{8}$ in. long, and the second was $11\frac{3}{8}$ in. long.

Cuban Tree Toad

How far did the toad jump in the two sand jumps? What was the difference between its two grass jumps?

a. Write what you know.

lengths of two sand jumps: ______ and ______

lengths of two grass jumps: ______ and ______

b. Write two number sentences.

______ + ______ = ______

______ − ______ = ______

Answer:

The toad jumped ______ in the sand.

The difference between its two grass jumps was ______.

Problem Solving Practice

2 Chuck's class has a Ricord's frog named Bob. Ricord's frogs are very poor jumpers. Chuck measured two of Bob's jumps. They were $4\frac{5}{8}$ in. long and $3\frac{1}{8}$ in. long.

How far did the frog jump?

What do you know?

____

____

____

The frog jumped a total distance of ______.

3 The world's biggest frog is the goliath frog from Cameroon in West Africa. Dr. Mbenga is studying a group of goliath frogs. The largest is $11\frac{5}{16}$ in. long. The smallest is $8\frac{1}{16}$ in. long.

How much bigger is the largest than the smallest?

What do you know?

____

____

The largest of Dr. Mbenga's frogs is ______ longer than the smallest.

4 You remember that Leaping Lena, the record-holding South African sharp-nosed frog, was 2 in. long. Chuck's frog Bob is $1\frac{13}{16}$ in. long.

How much longer was Leaping Lena than Bob?

____

Explain your answer.

____

____

____

____

____

____

5 An Asian tree frog built its nest $11\frac{1}{2}$ feet above the surface of a pond. When the tadpoles hatched, they fell $14\frac{1}{2}$ feet into the pond below.

How many feet did the level of the water drop between the time the nest was built and the time the eggs hatched?

____

Explain your answer.

____

____

____

____

LESSON 4

Understand Fraction and Percent Equivalents

Female Hamadryas Baboon

Baboon Bands Hamadryas baboons are found in Africa, in and around the country of Ethiopia. They live together in "troops," groups of 100 or more individuals. During the day, however, the baboons separate into smaller "bands" for feeding.

Bands are made up of several groups of one adult male and several females. Young males may hunt with a band or join together to form a "bachelor" band.

If a male stares directly at another male, that is a threat. To threaten back, the other male will show his huge canine teeth and expose his white eyelids. A grin with no exposed eyelids means fear.

Female Hamadryas baboons are olive brown, while males are silver-gray. However, if the females in one group leave to join other males, the remaining male's fur turns brown, just like a female's.

Give It a Try

In a single baboon troop, 20% of the individuals might be adult males. **What fraction of the troop is that?**

Meanwhile, $\frac{3}{5}$ of the individuals might be females. **What percentage of the troop is female?**

Create number sentences.

Remember that percent is the number of parts out of 100.

$20\% = \frac{\square}{\square}$

$\frac{3}{5} = \square\%$

- You can draw a diagram using unit squares to change fractions to percents and percents to fractions.
- Or, you can do calculations.

Approach 1: Draw a Diagram Using Unit Squares

To change a percent to a fraction:

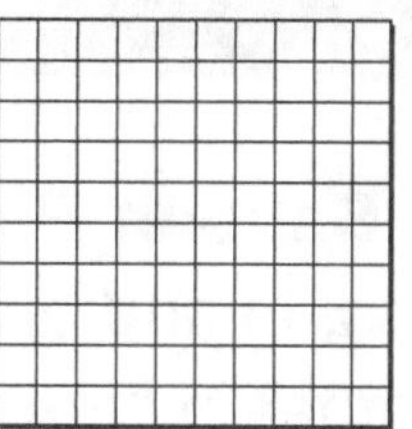

STEP 1 Draw 100 unit squares, then look at the percent and shade that number of squares.

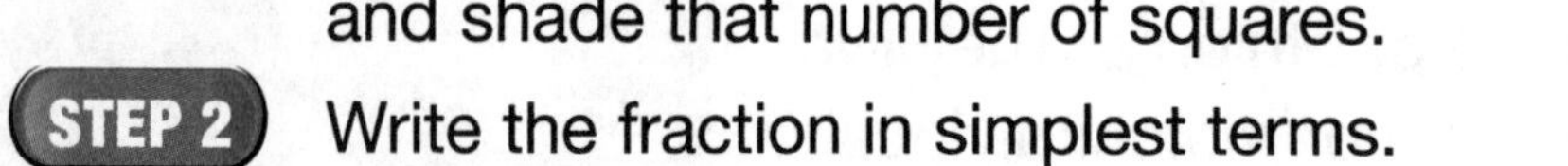

STEP 2 Write the fraction in simplest terms.

To change a fraction to a percent:

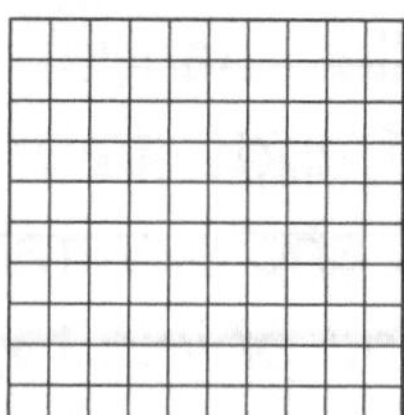

STEP 1 Draw 100 unit squares. For every 5 squares, shade 3.

STEP 2 The total number of shaded squares is the answer.

Approach 2: Do Calculations

To change a percent to a fraction:

STEP 1 Write the percent as a fraction with 100 as a denominator. $20\% = \frac{20}{100}$

STEP 2 Rewrite the fraction in simplest terms. $\frac{20}{100} \div \frac{20}{20} = \frac{1}{5}$

To change a fraction to a percent:

STEP 1 Set up the equivalent fractions. $\frac{3}{5} = \frac{\square}{100}$

STEP 2 Find the missing numerator. $\frac{3}{5} \times \frac{20}{20} = \frac{60}{100}$

STEP 3 Write the percent using the numerator you just found. **60%**

If 20% of the troop is adult males, what fraction of the troop is that?

$20\% = \frac{\square}{\square}$

If $\frac{3}{5}$ of the troop is females, what percentage of the troop is that?

$\frac{3}{5} = \square\%$

Practice This

Use the unit squares to write the equivalent fraction or percent.

1. 45% = $\frac{\square}{\square}$

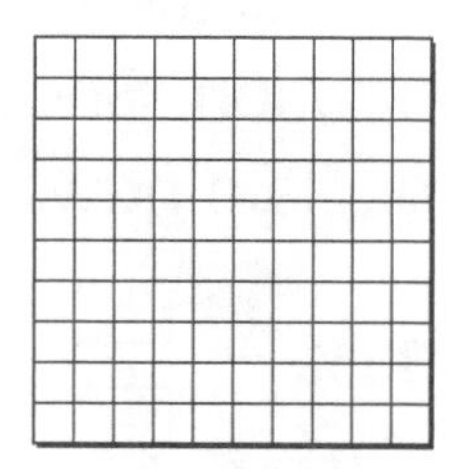

2. 12% = $\frac{\square}{\square}$

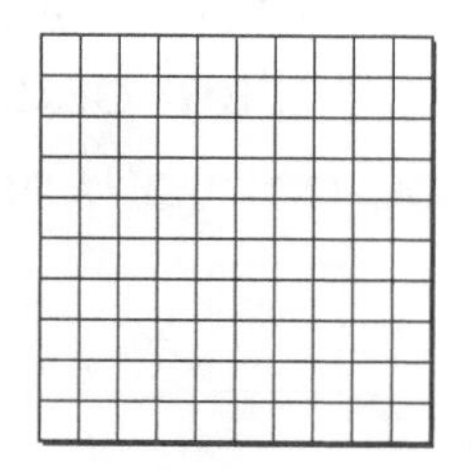

3. $\frac{13}{20}$ = ☐

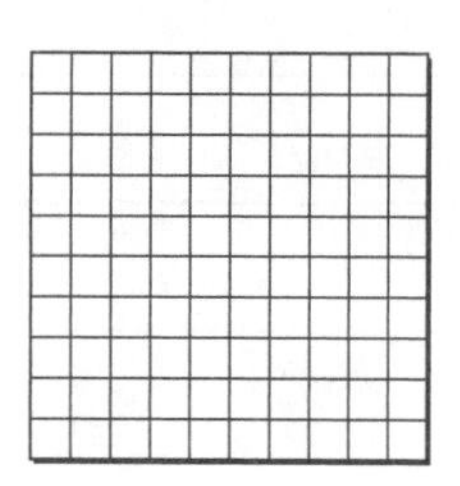

4. $\frac{3}{10}$ = ☐

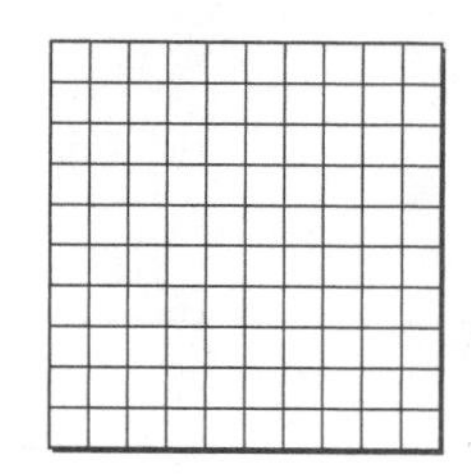

Write the equivalent fraction or percent.

5. 75% = $\frac{\square}{\square}$
6. 3% = $\frac{\square}{\square}$
7. $\frac{39}{50}$ = ☐%
8. $\frac{1}{4}$ = ☐%
9. $\frac{1}{2}$ = ☐%
10. $\frac{16}{25}$ = ☐%
11. $\frac{7}{10}$ = ☐%
12. 66% = $\frac{\square}{\square}$
13. 84% = $\frac{\square}{\square}$
14. 10% = $\frac{\square}{\square}$
15. 92% = $\frac{\square}{\square}$
16. 38% = $\frac{\square}{\square}$

Practice This

Write the equivalent fraction or percent.

17 Use the unit squares to find the equivalent percent. Explain how you got your answer.

$\frac{3}{4}$ = ☐ %

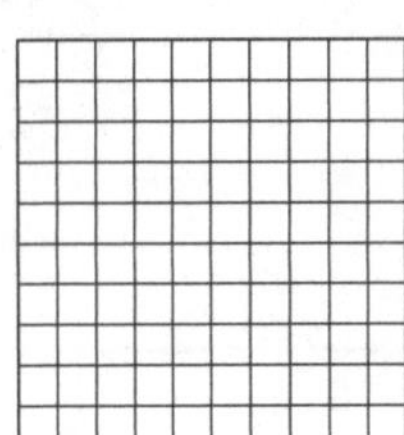

18 Calculate to find the equivalent fraction. Show your work and explain how you got your answer.

35% $= \frac{☐}{☐}$

19 Each answer box has either a fraction or a percent under it. If there is a fraction, find the equivalent percent. If there is a percent, find the equivalent fraction. Then locate that equivalent fraction or percent in the shaded box. Look at the letter above it, and write that letter in the answer box.

When you are done, you will have the answer to the question:

Where do baboons sleep?

☐ $\frac{9}{150}$ ☐ 95% ☐ $\frac{2}{5}$ ☐ 54% ☐ 36%

☐ $\frac{13}{20}$ ☐ 75% ☐ $\frac{21}{25}$ ☐ $\frac{84}{100}$

OR

☐ $\frac{6}{15}$ ☐ $\frac{42}{50}$ ☐ 40% ☐ $\frac{7}{20}$ ☐ $\frac{35}{100}$ ☐ $\frac{35}{50}$

☐ $\frac{78}{120}$ ☐ $\frac{3}{50}$ ☐ $\frac{1}{10}$ ☐ $\frac{3}{30}$ ☐ $\frac{7}{10}$

A	B	C	D	E	F	G
$\frac{3}{4}$	37%	40%	$\frac{3}{8}$	10%	35%	100%
H	**I**	**J**	**K**	**L**	**M**	**N**
$\frac{7}{8}$	$\frac{2}{5}$	1%	$\frac{27}{50}$	84%	$\frac{5}{6}$	$\frac{11}{15}$
O	**P**	**Q**	**R**	**S**	**T**	**U**
$\frac{19}{20}$	50%	98%	6%	70%	65%	$\frac{3}{16}$
V	**W**	**X**	**Y**	**Z**		
$\frac{2}{3}$	$\frac{1}{6}$	0%	$\frac{9}{25}$	$\frac{1}{3}$		

Problem Solving

Baboons prefer to eat fruit, but they will eat whatever is around if they have to. They can stuff a large amount of food in their cheek pockets, and then carry it somewhere safe to eat it.

Solve.

1 During the dry season, grass can make up 90% of a baboon's diet. They can also survive on nothing but roots, bulbs, and tubers. Their large, broad teeth allow them to chew these tough plant parts.

What fraction of a baboon's diet might be made up of grass during the dry season?

a. Write what you know.

percent of a baboon's diet: ____________

b. Write a number sentence.

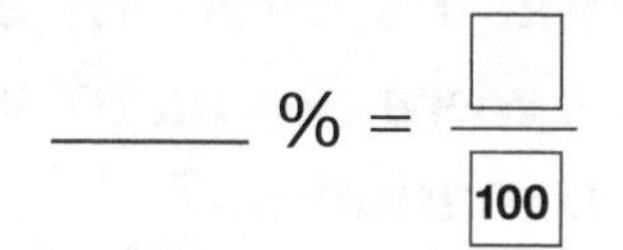

_____ % = $\frac{\square}{100}$

Answer:

During the dry season, grass can make up 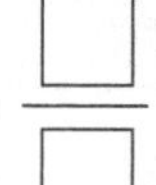 $\frac{\square}{\square}$ of a baboon's diet.

Problem Solving Practice

2 One troop of baboons lives in an area of about 60 sq km. One day, a troop travels 25 km looking for food. They covered 15 km before noon.

What fraction of the total distance is the distance covered before noon? What percent?

What do you know?

____

____

The baboons traveled ______ or ______ of the total distance before noon.

3 The Hamadryas baboon is the smallest of all baboons. But it has a very long tail. One Hamadryas baboon has a tail that is 55 cm long. Without the tail, its head and body are 70 centimeters long.

What fraction of its total length is made up of tail? What percentage?

What do you know?

____

____

The baboon's tail makes up ______ or ______ of its total length.

4 Maria's science class searched the Internet for pictures of baboons. Of the 200 pictures they downloaded, only 44 showed a Guinea baboon.

What fraction of the photos showed a Guinea baboon? What percent?

____

Explain your answer.

____

____

____

____

____

5 Over the course of a week, a troop of Chacma baboons ate grasses, roots, leaves, buds, flowers, fruits, seeds, twigs, bark, scorpions, grasshoppers, spiders, crabs, lizards, turtles, frogs, fish, and an antelope.

Of all the items the baboons ate, what percent were animals? What fraction were mammals?

____

Explain your answer.

____

____

____

LESSON 5 Use Mathematical Properties to Solve Problems

Rotting Fish + Burned Sugar = Beetles + Bees

The world's largest flower is also the stinkiest. The Titan arum grows in the rain forests of Sumatra in Indonesia. The plant might go for years, or even decades, without producing a flower. But when a flower does appear, it is spectacular. It is shaped like an upside-down bell, and is nearly 10 feet around at the top! The inside of the flower is dark red and looks like rotting meat. The odor it gives off smells like a mix of rotting fish and burned sugar.

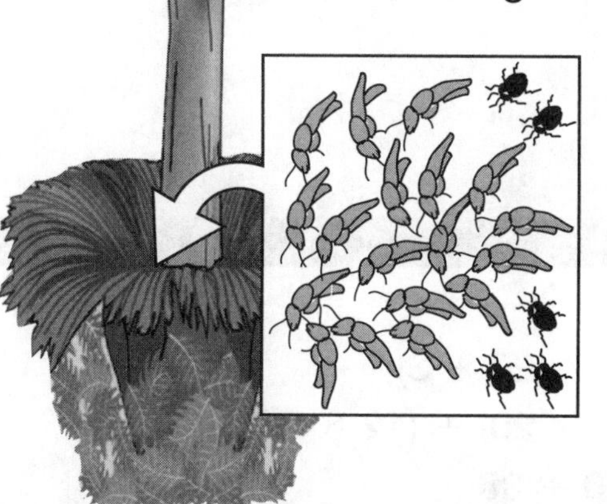

The smell attracts insects that eat decaying meat, such as carrion beetles and sweat bees. They carry pollen from one Titan arum plant to another.

In a few days, the blossom wilts away. All that remains is a single leaf, 20 feet tall and 15 feet across. It takes many years for the plant to build up the strength, and the stink, to bloom again!

Give It a Try

There are 12 Titan arums in this part of the rain forest. **If they all have the same number of insects on them, what is the total number of insects on all the plants?**

Carrion beetles, like all insects, have 6 legs. **What is the total number of carrion-beetle legs on all the plants?**

Mathematical properties can make the calculations much easier.

Create number sentences.

$23 \times 12 =$ ☐

$12 \times 5 \times 6 =$ ☐

- You can simply do the arithmetic to find the solutions.
- Or, you can use mathematical properties before you do the calculations.

Approach 1: Do the Arithmetic

STEP 1 Multiply.

STEP 2 Add.

$$\begin{array}{r} 12 \\ \times\ 23 \\ \hline 36 \\ 240 \end{array} \qquad \begin{array}{r} 12 \\ \times\ 23 \\ \hline 36 \\ 240 \\ \hline 276 \end{array}$$

STEP 1 Multiply the first pair of numbers.

STEP 2 Multiply the product by the third number.

$$\begin{array}{r} 12 \\ \times\ \ 5 \\ \hline 60 \end{array} \qquad \begin{array}{r} 60 \\ \times\ \ 6 \\ \hline 360 \end{array}$$

Approach 2: Use Mathematical Properties and Then Do the Arithmetic

STEP 1 Use the Distributive Property.

STEP 2 Multiply and then add.

$$\begin{aligned} 12 \times 23 &= 12 \times (20 + 3) \\ &= (12 \times 20) + (12 \times 3) \\ &= 240 + 36 \\ &= 276 \end{aligned}$$

STEP 1 Use the Associative Property.

STEP 2 Choose one of the equations and multiply.

$$12 \times 5 \times 6 = 12 \times (5 \times 6) = (12 \times 5) \times 6$$
$$12 \times 30 = 60 \times 6$$
$$360 = 360$$

What is the total number of insects on all the plants?

$23 \times 12 = \square$

What is the total number of carrion-beetle legs on all the plants?

$12 \times 5 \times 6 = \square$

Practice This

Use the Distributive Property to solve.

1. $12 \times 31 = \square$

   $12 \times 30 = \bigcirc$

   $12 \times 1 = \triangle$

   $\bigcirc + \triangle = \square$

2. $7 \times 56 = \square$

   $7 \times 50 = \bigcirc$

   $7 \times 6 = \triangle$

   $\bigcirc + \triangle = \square$

3. $6 \times 315 = \square$

   $6 \times 300 = \bigcirc$

   $6 \times 10 = \triangle$

   $6 \times 5 = \hexagon$

   $\bigcirc + \triangle + \hexagon = \square$

4. $9 \times 31 = \square$
5. $8 \times 27 = \square$
6. $5 \times 292 = \square$
7. $3 \times 88 = \square$
8. $4 \times 44 = \square$
9. $2 \times 237 = \square$

Use the Associative Property to solve.

10. $(18 \times 4) \times 5 =$

    $18 \times (\square \times \square) = \square$

11. $(8 \times 6) \times 10 =$

    $8 \times (\square \times \square) = \square$

12. $(11 \times 2) \times 4 =$

    $11 \times (\square \times \square) = \square$

13. $(6 \times 5) \times 3 = \square$
14. $(11 \times 5) \times 5 = \square$
15. $(7 \times 12) \times 10 = \square$
16. $(4 \times 5) \times 2 = \square$
17. $(9 \times 9) \times 20 = \square$
18. $6 \times 10 \times 8 \times 5 = \square$

Practice This

Solve.

19 Use the Distributive Property to find the product. Explain how you got your answer.

$24 \times 8 = \square$

____

____

____

____

20 Use the Associative Property to find the product. Explain how you got your answer.

$(9 \times 3) \times 20 = 9 \times (\square \times \square) = \square$

____

____

____

____

21 When do 20 petals make up a whole flower? Or, to put in it math terms, when does

$20 \times (P + E + T + A + L) = F + L + O + W + E + R$

A = 2	P = 5
E = 1	R = 31
F = 140	T = 9
L = 3	W = 200
O = 25	

Use the code in the box to substitute a number for each letter. Then perform the calculations to see if the number sentence is true. You may want to use one or more mathematical properties to make the calculations easier.

$20 \times (\square + \square + \square + \square + \square) = \square + \square + \square + \square + \square + \square$

Now see if you can make up your own number sentence using letters. Start by making up the sentence with letters. For example, $2 \times (S + O + C + K) = P + A + I + R$. Then substitute a value for each letter that will make the sentence true.

Problem Solving

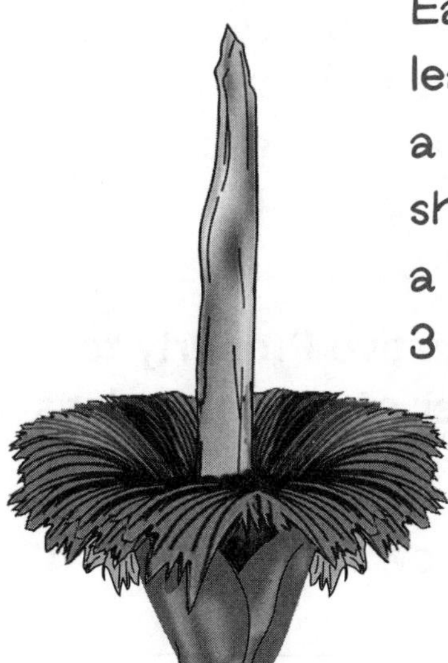

Each fall, the Titan arum's leaf falls back. In the spring, a new shoot pushes up. The shoot cannot be identified as a leaf or a flower until it is 3 or 4 feet tall.

Solve.

1 One day, the gardeners at the Gibbons Arboretum (ar•buh•REE•tum) notice a swelling at the bottom of the shoot. That tells them the shoot will grow into a flower. For the next 3 days, the shoot grows at a rate of 4 inches per day. For the following 3 days, it grows 8 inches each day.

How much did the plant grow over those 6 days?

a. Write what you know.

first 3 days: ____________ each day

second 3 days: ____________ each day

b. Write a number sentence.

$(\mathbf{3} \times \square) + (\mathbf{3} \times \square) = \mathbf{3} \times (\square + \square)$

Answer:

Over those 6 days, the Titan arum grew a total of ______ inches.

Problem Solving Practice

2 The Titan arum leaf divides into three parts. Each part is divided into leaflets. One day there are 25 leaflets on each part of the leaf. The next day there are 5 more leaflets on each part of the leaf.

Use the Distributive Property to find the number of leaflets on the entire leaf.

What do you know?

____

____

There would be _____ total leaflets.

3 The arboretum is made up of 6 rooms. Each room has 3 outside walls, and each outside wall has 5 windows. Each window contains 24 panes of glass.

Use the Associative Property to find the number of panes of glass in the entire arboretum.

What do you know?

____

____

There are _____ panes of glass in the entire arboretum.

4 At the arboretum, each of the 4 Titan arums is planted in its own large container. Each container holds 437 pounds of dirt.

How much dirt is there in all the containers?

____

Explain how you used mathematical properties to find the answer.

____

____

____

____

____

____

5 Outside the arboretum there are 4 gardens. Each garden has 3 Cherry Dogwood trees that are beginning to bloom. There are 5 main branches on each tree. Each of these branches has 25 flowers in bloom.

What is the total number of flowers in bloom?

____

Explain how you used mathematical properties to find the answer.

____

____

____

____

Solve for Unknowns in Algebraic Equations

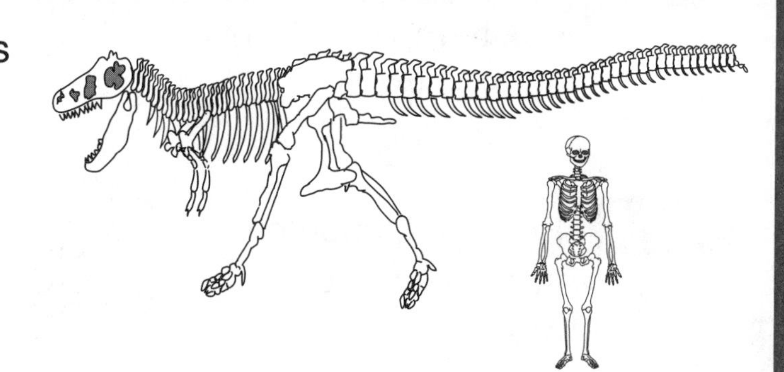

Boning Up on Bones The bones in your body are living structures. Bones can support great weight, but that's not all they do. Inside some of your bones is a substance called marrow. Marrow produces blood cells. In fact, it produces 2.6 million new red blood cells per second!

Babies have 300 different bones. But as the baby grows, some bones join together. An 18-year-old has only 206 separate bones. With old age, the bones of the spine squish closer together. A person can shrink by a half-inch or more.

Do large animals have more bones in their skeleton? No. A human has the same number of neck bones as a giraffe. And a gigantic Tyrannosaurus Rex had the same number of bones as a human baby does.

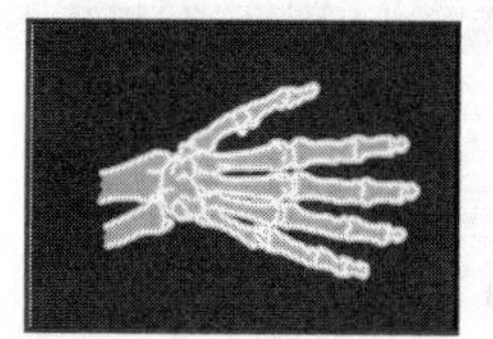

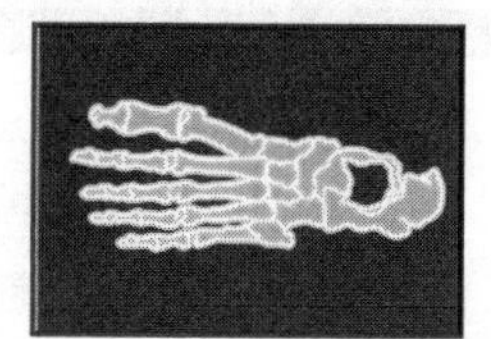

Human hand and foot.

Give It a Try

You have 27 bones in your hand—8 of them are in your wrist, and 5 are in your palm.

How many bones are in your fingers?

Create a number sentence.

For this problem you can use 27 counters.

$8 + 5 + \square = 27$

- You can use counters to find the answer.
- Or, you can use algebra.

Approach 1: Use Counters

STEP 1 Illustrate the problem with counters. Use a box to represent the number you're looking for.

STEP 2 Remove 8 counters from the group of 27.

STEP 3 Remove 5 more counters from the group. What remains is your answer.

You can count the counters to check your answer as well.

Approach 2: Use Algebra

STEP 1 Write the equation. Use x to represent the number you're looking for.

STEP 2 Start by adding 8 and 5.

STEP 3 Subtract 13 from both sides of the equation. (As long as you perform the same operation on each side, the equation remains true.)

You can easily check your answer.

$$8 + 5 + x = 27$$

$$13 + x = 27$$

$$13 - 13 + x = 27 - 13$$

$$x = 14$$

$$8 + 5 + 14 = 27$$

You have 27 bones in your hand—8 of them are in your wrist, and 5 are in your palm. How many bones are in your fingers?

There are _____ bones in my fingers.

Practice This

Use the counters to solve.

1 $15 + 9 + x = 36$

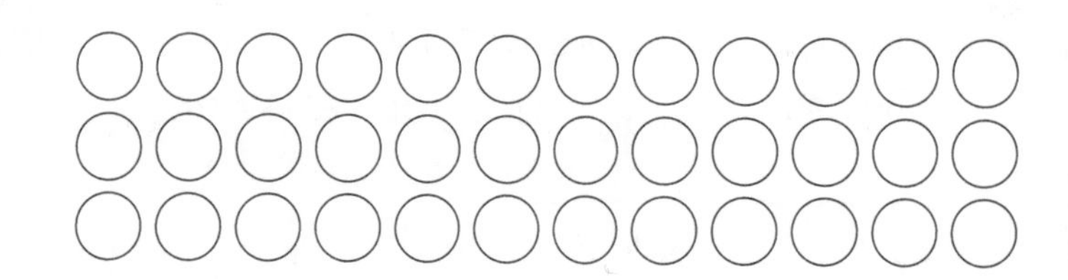

2 $15 + r + 4 = 25$

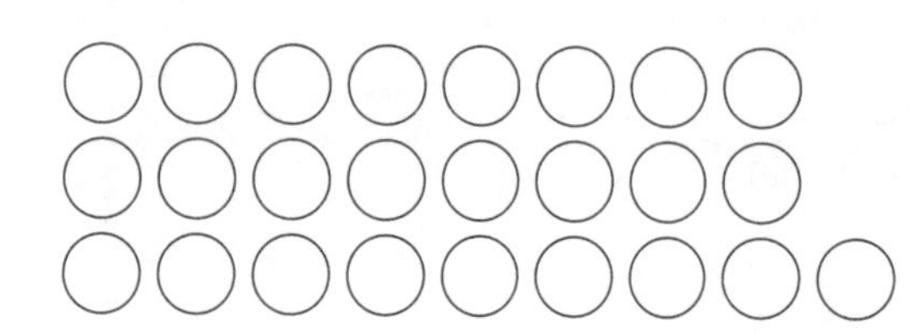

3 $y - 5 = 23$

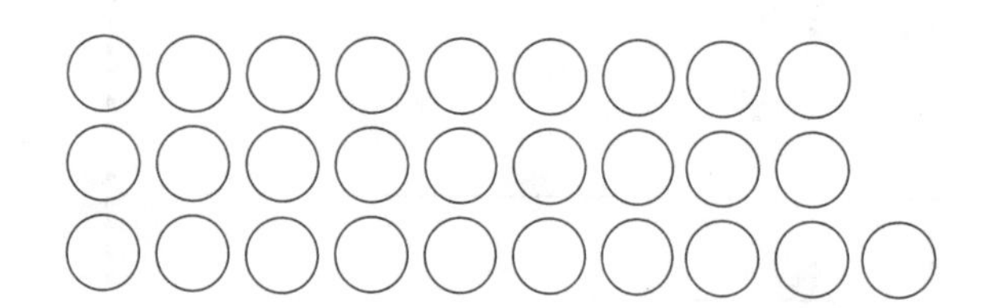

Use algebra to solve.

4 $79 + y = 112$

$79 - 79 + y = 112 - 79$

$y =$ ☐

5 $k \times 9 = 27$

$k \times 9 \div 9 = 27 \div 9$

$k =$ ☐

6 $v \div 11 = 12$

$v \div 11 \times 11 = 12 \times 11$

$v =$ ☐

7 $145 + d = 333$

$d =$ ☐

8 $z \times 5 = 565$

$z =$ ☐

9 $a \times 4 = 60$

$a =$ ☐

10 $4 + m = 6$

$m =$ ☐

11 $m \div 7 = 12$

$m =$ ☐

12 $d \div 20 = 33$

$d =$ ☐

13 $g - 247 = 591$

$g =$ ☐

14 $t - 522 = 89$

$t =$ ☐

15 $19 + 47 + n = 5{,}211$

$n =$ ☐

Practice This

Solve.

16 Use the counters to solve.
Explain how you got your answer.

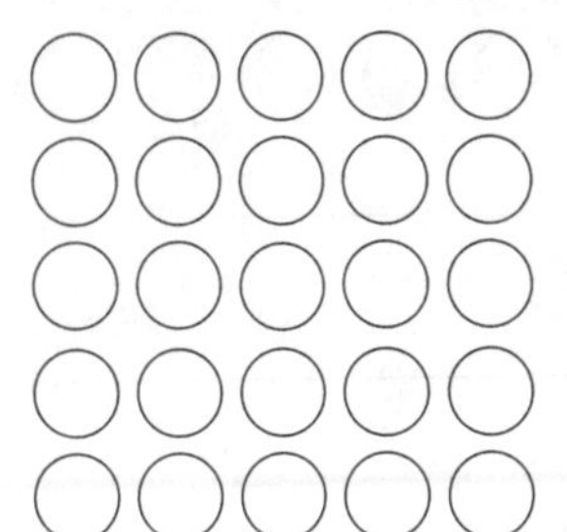

$x + 14 = 25$

____

____

____

17 Use algebra to solve.
Explain how you got your answer.

$x \div 3 = 16$

____

____

____

____

____

____

____

18 Break the code by substituting a number for each shape. The numbers you use must make every number sentence true.

8 + ○ = 10

⬡ × ○ = 12

⬡ ÷ ⬡ = ⌂

⌂ − ⌂ = △

19 Decode the sentence below by substituting the number you found for each shape.

The smallest bone in the human body is the stirrup bone behind your eardrum.

It is only  **millimeters long!**

Problem Solving

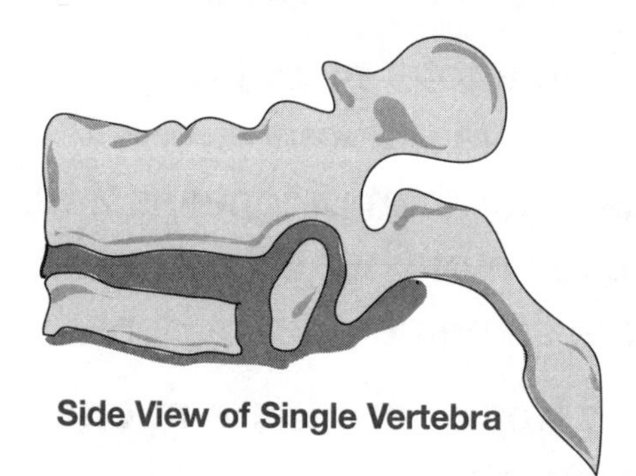
Side View of Single Vertebra

The spine is made up of 33 small bones called vertebrae. These bones, which have a space at their center, surround and protect the spinal cord. The spinal cord is a bundle of nerves that goes from your brain down the center of your back.

Solve.

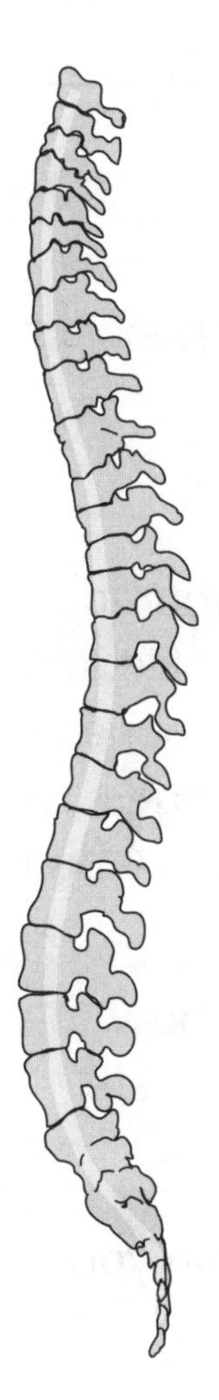

1 As mentioned above, the spine is made up of 33 vertebrae. The spine can be divided into 5 sections. The top or first section consists of 7 vertebrae. The second section consists of 12 vertebrae, the third section consists of 5 vertebrae, and the fourth section consists of 5 vertebrae.

How many vertebrae are in the bottom, or fifth, section of the spine?

a. Write what you know.

total number of vertebrae: ________

number of vertebrae in first section: ________

number of vertebrae in second section: ________

number of vertebrae in third section: ________

number of vertebrae in fourth section: ________

b. Write a number sentence.

$\square + \square + \square + \square + \boldsymbol{x} = \square$

Answer:

The bottom, or fifth, section of the spine contains a total of ______ vertebrae.

Problem Solving Practice

2 The rib cage is made up of pairs of ribs. Most people have a total of 24 ribs.

How many pairs of ribs do most people have?

What do you know?

____

____

____

____

Most people have ______ pairs of ribs.

3 You have a total of 14 bones in the fingers on one of your hands. Your thumb contains 2 of them. Each of your other fingers has the same number of bones.

How many bones are there in one of your other fingers?

What do you know?

____

____

____

There are ______ bones in one of your fingers.

4 Your foot is made up of your ankle, arch, and toes. There are 5 bones in your arch. Like your fingers, your toes contain a total of 14 bones.

If there are 26 bones in your entire foot, how many of them are in your ankle?

____

Explain your answer.

____

____

____

____

____

____

5 There are 3 bones in your arm. The bone in your upper arm is called the humerus. The bottom of the humerus protects the ulnar nerve. Banging your elbow stimulates the ulnar nerve and produces a tingling sensation. So your "funny bone" is really a nerve.

How many bones are in your lower arm?

____

Explain your answer.

____

____

____

Make Comparisons with Perimeter and Area

The World's Tallest and Largest Trees The tallest tree in the world is a Coastal Redwood called the Mendocino Tree. It measures 368 feet high. That's over 60 feet taller than the Statue of Liberty!

Oddly, the Mendocino Tree is not the largest tree in the world. That honor goes to a giant sequoia called General Sherman. General Sherman is only 272 feet tall. So how is it larger than the Mendocino Tree? The Mendocino Tree is only 10 feet across. General Sherman, on the other hand, measures over 36 feet across.

It's hard to truly understand how large these trees are. Consider this: In 1978, a dead branch fell off General Sherman. It was over 140 feet long and had a diameter of more than 25 feet. This one branch was larger than almost any tree in the eastern United States!

General Sherman Sequoia Tree

Give It a Try

Today, these trees are protected. But, to understand how big these trees are, imagine you made boards from the trunks of the General Sherman and the Mendocino Tree.

Which would have the larger perimeter? Which would have the larger area?

- You can use addition to find the perimeters, then multiplication to find the areas.
- Or, you can use the formula $P = 2(\ell + w)$ to find the perimeters, and the formula $A = \ell \times w$ to find the areas.

Perimeter *Perimeter* is the distance around the edge. *Area* is the size of the surface. A tree *trunk* is the main stem of a tree.

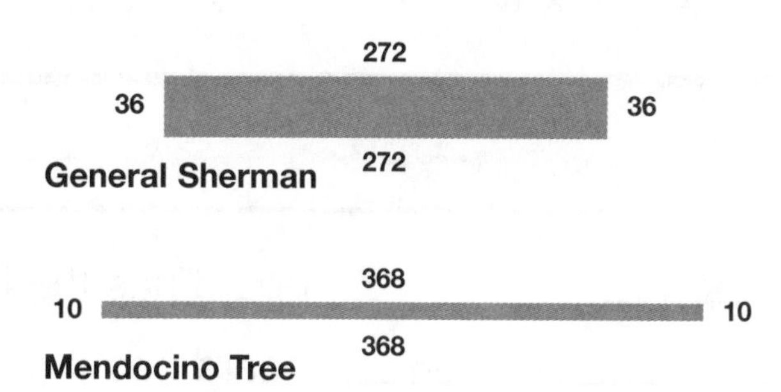

Approach 1: Use Addition to Find Perimeter and Multiplication to Find Area

STEP 1 For each board, list the lengths of all four sides.

STEP 2 Add the lengths together.

Board from General Sherman: **272 ft + 36 ft + 272 ft + 36 ft = 616 ft**

Board from Mendocino Tree: **368 ft + 10 ft + 368 ft + 10 ft = 756 ft**

STEP 3 To find the area of each board, multiply the lengths of two adjacent sides.

Board from General Sherman: **272 ft × 36 ft = 9,792 sq ft**

Board from Mendocino Tree: **368 ft × 10 ft = 3,680 sq ft**

Approach 2: Use Formulas

STEP 1 For each board, plug the correct numbers into each formula.

STEP 2 Calculate to find the perimeters and the areas.

Board from General Sherman:
$P = 2(\ell + w)$ $P = 2(272 + 36)$ $P = 2(308) = 616$ ft

Board from Mendocino Tree:
$P = 2(\ell + w)$ $P = 2(368 + 10)$ $P = 2(378) = 756$ ft

Board from General Sherman:
$A = \ell \times w$ $A = 272 \times 36$ $A = 9{,}792$ sq ft

Board from Mendocino Tree:
$A = \ell \times w$ $A = 368 \times 10$ $A = 3{,}680$ sq ft

The ______________________ board has the larger perimeter.

The ______________________ board has the larger area.

Practice This

Use addition to find the perimeters and multiplication to find the areas.

1. Board A **Perimeter** = ☐ + ☐ + ☐ + ☐ = ☐

   Area = ☐ × ☐ = ☐

2. Board B **Perimeter** = ☐ + ☐ + ☐ + ☐ = ☐

   Area = ☐ × ☐ = ☐

3. Which board has the smallest perimeter? ______

   The smallest area? ______

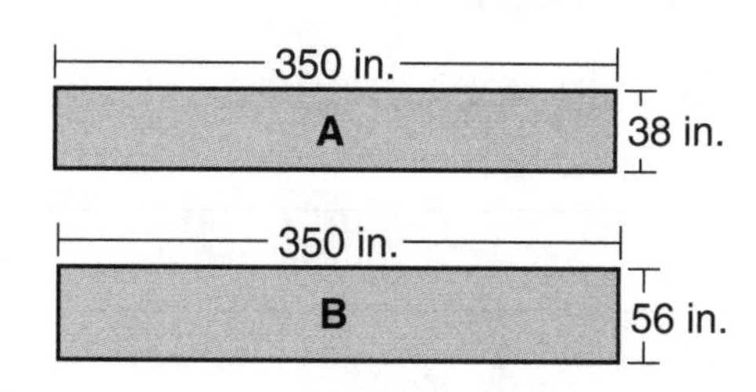

Use formulas to find the perimeters and the areas.

4. Board C

   $P = 2(\ell + w) = 2(\square + \square) = 2(\square) = \square$

   $A = \ell \times w = \square \times \square = \square$

5. Board D

   $P = 2(\ell + w) = 2(\square + \square) = 2(\square) = \square$

   $A = \ell \times w = \square \times \square = \square$

6. Board E

   $P = 2(\ell + w) = 2(\square + \square) = 2(\square) = \square$

   $A = \ell \times w = \square \times \square = \square$

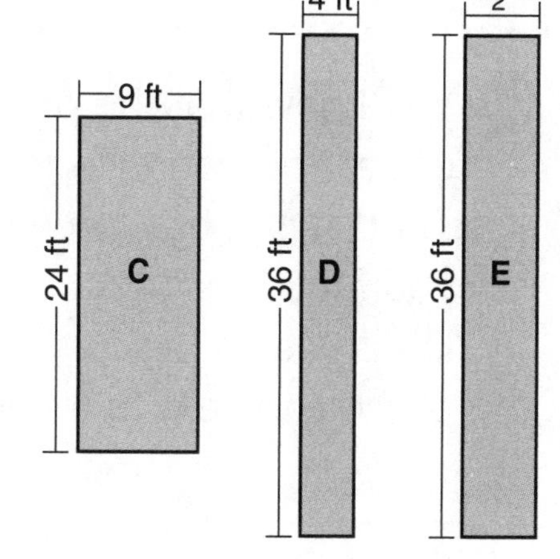

7. Which board has the largest perimeter? ______

   The largest area? ______

Practice This

Solve.

8 Forestry students are mapping a rectangular section of a coastal redwood's root system. The section is 9 feet wide and 98 feet long.

How large an area are they mapping?

Explain your answer.

____

____

____

____

9 Giant sequoia once grew all over Europe and North America. Today there are only 75 groves of giant sequoias, all in California.

If one side of a rectangular 4,000-square yard grove is 125 yards long, what is its perimeter?

Explain your answer.

____

____

____

____

10 You know that the perimeter of a shape is the distance around its edge. You can take that distance and straighten it to form a line. That's what has been done with the four rectangles below. Can you match each rectangle with the line that is about the same length as its perimeter? You may use a ruler. Write the number of the line next to the letter of the rectangle.

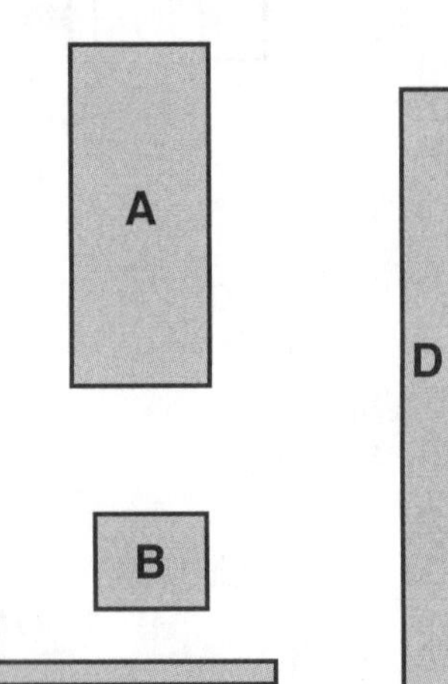

1. ______________

2. ______________________

3. ________________________________

4. ____

Problem Solving

Since the mid-1880s, people have been cutting down giant sequoias. The wood was used for shingles and fences but was finally considered to be too brittle. Today, most giant sequoias are protected in national or state parks.

Solve.

1. Before these trees were protected, one of the first giant sequoias to be cut down was called the Mark Twain tree. Its stump—the part that is left over when a tree is cut down—was so large, some people held a dance on it. They had a band, 32 dancers, and even spectators!

   Imagine it is up to you to build a dance floor on a stump the size of the stump of a Mark Twain tree. You can build a square floor that measures 21 feet by 21 feet or a rectangular one that measures 23 feet by 16 feet.

   Which dance floor will have the greater area? The greater perimeter?

   a. Write what you know.

   dimensions of square dance floor: ________

   dimensions of rectangular dance floor: ________

   b. Write number sentences.

   area of square dance floor = ________

   area of rectangular dance floor = ________

   perimeter of square dance floor = ________

   perimeter of rectangular dance floor = ________

Answers:

The ____________ dance floor has the greater area.

The ____________ dance floor has the greater perimeter.

Problem Solving Practice

2 A board has a perimeter of 36 feet.

What is the largest area it could have?

What do you know?

____

____

____

____

The largest area it could have is __________.

3 A board has an area of 150 square feet.

Name 2 possible perimeters for the board.

What do you know?

____

____

____

____

Two possible perimeters are __________ and __________.

4 A carpenter is building two redwood decks. One is 8 feet deep and 6 feet wide. The second one has the same perimeter as the first, but its area is 8 square feet smaller.

What are the dimensions of the second deck?

____

Explain your answer.

____

____

____

____

____

____

5 Imagine you took a board from the trunk of a Dyerville Giant tree and a eucalyptus tree. The board from the Dyerville Giant is 360 feet long and 17 feet wide. The board from the eucalyptus tree is 408 feet long.

How wide would it have to be in order to have the same area as the Dyerville Giant's board?

____

Explain your answer.

____

____

____

____

____

LESSON 8 Use a Coordinate Grid to Find Directions

A Coyote's Secret Den If you hear something howling in the night, it just may be the sound of a coyote. The howl of a male coyote is a familiar sound in the desert or open country. It is his way of communicating with other coyotes. A coyote's howl may be welcoming females in the area, or it may be warning other males to stay away.

Coyotes eat just about anything. They can adapt to many different surroundings. Coyotes love mice and other rodents. But they will gladly settle for lizards, fish, insects, even nuts and berries. Coyotes sometimes work in pairs or teams. One coyote will run around to distract birds while another coyote will sneak up and attack.

Give It a Try

Scientists track coyotes by marking the locations of their dens on coordinate grids.

On the coordinate grid, find the coyote's den, which is located at (3, 1).

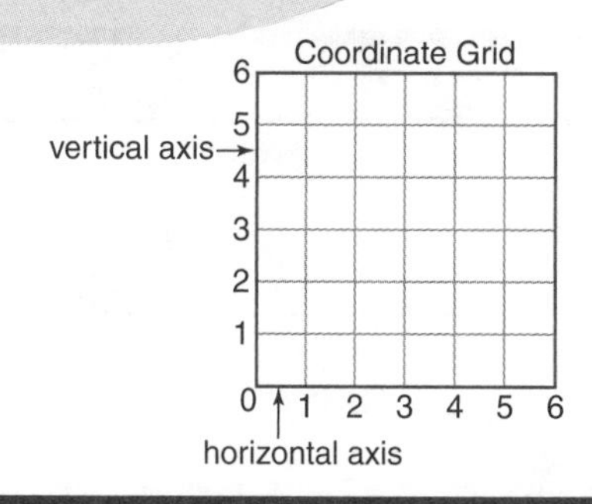

First coordinate is on the horizontal axis = ☐.

"Coordinate" means two numbers working together.

Second coordinate is on the vertical axis = ☐.

The numbers on each axis help you find the coordinate pair.

- Move left or right along the **horizontal axis** to find the first coordinate.
- Move up or down along the **vertical axis** to find the second coordinate.

Reminder

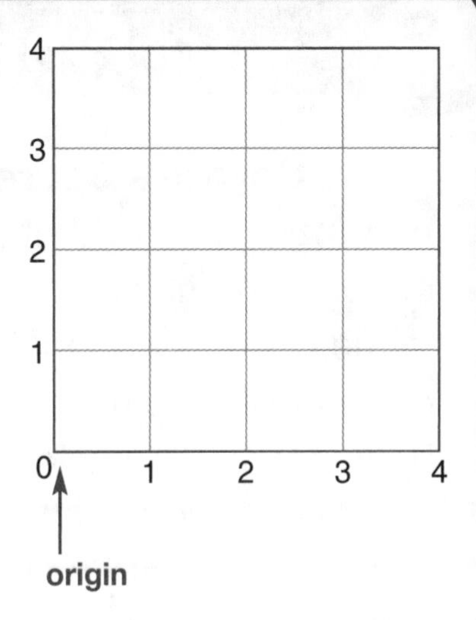

A **coordinate grid** is formed by 2 axes or number lines:

- a horizontal axis that goes left and right
- a vertical axis that goes up and down

A **coordinate pair** identifies the location of a point on a coordinate grid. It is written like this: (3, 1).

- The first number (**3**, 1) tells the number of units from the origin on the horizontal axis.
- The second number (3, **1**) tells the number of units from the origin on the vertical axis.

Step by Step

STEP 1 Start at 0. This is the **origin**. The coordinate pair is (0, 0).

STEP 2 To find the coordinate pair (3, 1), look at the first number, **3**, and move 3 units to the right.

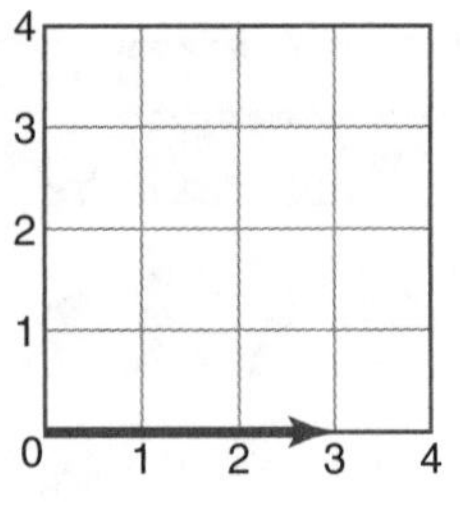

STEP 3 Look at the second number in (3, **1**). The second number, **1**, tells you to move up 1 unit.

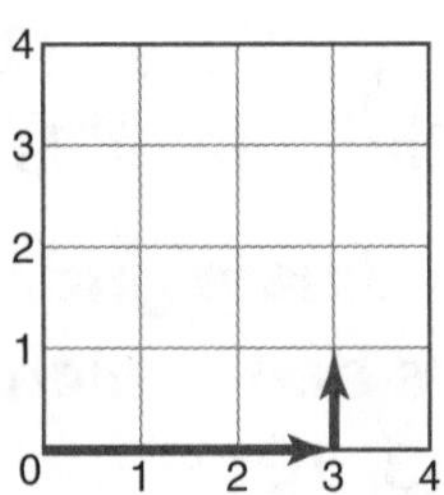

Find the coyote den, which is located at (3, 1).

The coyote den is located at ____________ on the ____________ axis.

It is also located at ____________ on the ____________ axis.

Practice This

On the coordinate grid, draw the points of these coordinate pairs. Label each point.

1. **Point A (3, 1)**
2. **Point B (4, 1)**
3. **Point C (5, 4)**
4. **Point D (2, 4)**
5. Connect the points you have marked in order, to form a shape. A coyote has its den somewhere in the middle of the shape on the grid. What coordinates could show the location of the coyote's den? ______

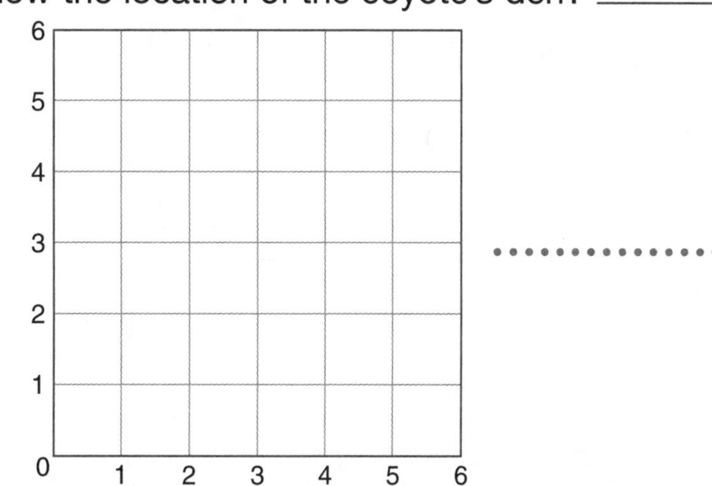

On the coordinate grid, draw the points for each coordinate pair below. Tell how many units you have to move to get from one point to the other.

6. Starting point: (1, 2)
   New point: (2, 3)
   Move left or right = ______
   Move up or down = ______

7. Starting point: (2, 4)
   New point: (4, 5)
   Move left or right = ______
   Move up or down = ______

8. Starting point: (3, 1)
   New point: (6, 4)
   Move left or right = ______
   Move up or down = ______

9. Starting point: (4, 1)
   New point: (6, 3)
   Move left or right = ______
   Move up or down = ______

10. Starting point: (5, 1)
    New point: (5, 5)
    Move left or right = ______
    Move up or down = ______

11. Starting point: (1, 4)
    New point: (4, 3)
    Move left or right = ______
    Move up or down = ______

Practice This

12 A coyote is spotted at **(1, 5)**. It is going after a rabbit located at **(3, 3)**. Then it will head back to its den at **(5, 4)**. The next day it is spotted again at **(1, 5)**.

Mark and label these 3 points on the grid. Then describe the path that the coyote takes.

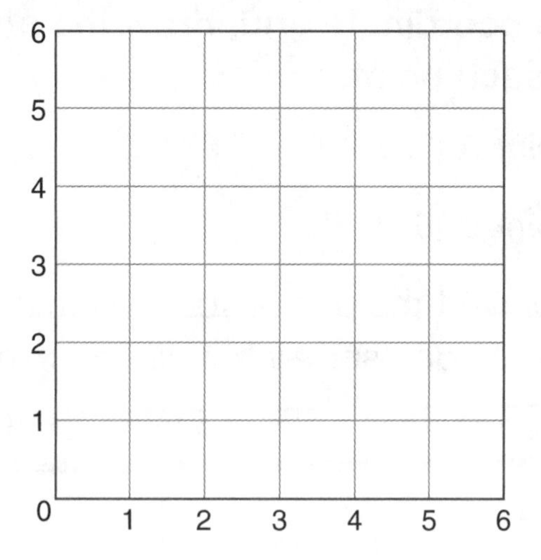

____

____

____

____

____

____

____

13 Mark these points on the grid. Draw lines to connect the points as you mark them. Then solve the riddle.

(3, 0) (3, 1) (1, 1) (2, 2) (1, 2) (2, 3) (1, 3)

(2, 4) (3, 5) (4, 5) (5, 4) (6, 3) (5, 3) (6, 2)

(5, 2) (6, 1) (4, 1) (4, 0)

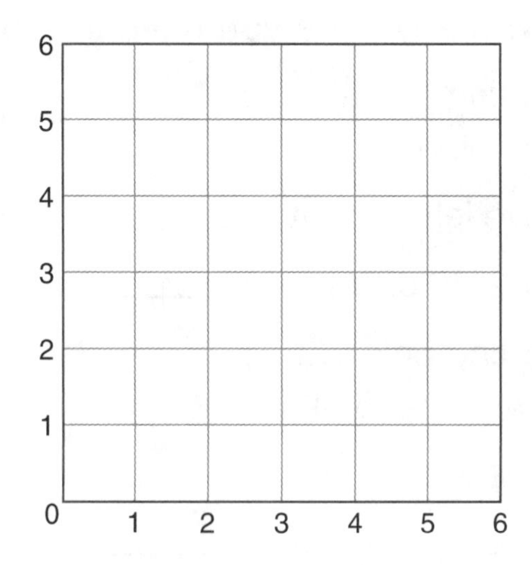

Riddle **What is one thing that coyotes have a hard time climbing?**

____

Problem Solving

Coyotes are known as prairie or brush dogs. They are also called desert wolves, even though they are not wolves. Lately, some coyotes have started moving away from the desert and toward areas inhabited by people.

Use the coordinate grid to solve.

1 Coyotes will go anywhere to find food. They will eat almost anything, even garbage tossed out by humans. However, coyotes are not good climbers and can't get food from high places, such as trees.

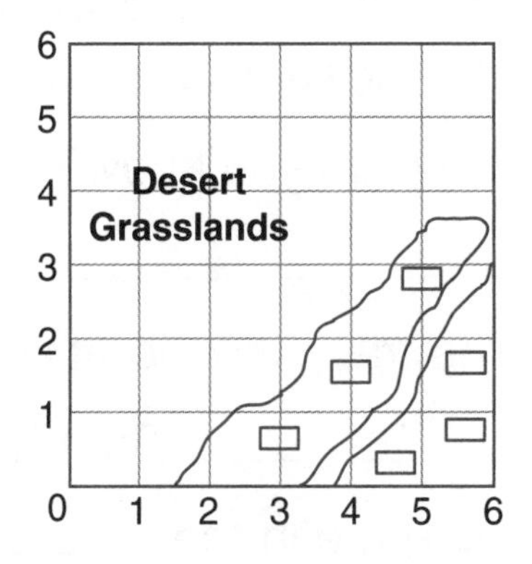

Coyote X has been seen at (4, 2). Coyote Z has been seen at (4, 5). Which coyote is closer to humans?

a. Write what you know.

location of Coyote X = ____________

location of Coyote Z = ____________

b. The areas marked on the grid show where humans live and where the desert is. Mark the points on the grid to show where each coyote has been spotted.

(4, 2) is in ____________ area.

(4, 5) is in ____________ area.

Answers:

Coyote X has been seen in ___________ area.

Coyote Z has been seen in ___________ area.

Problem Solving Practice

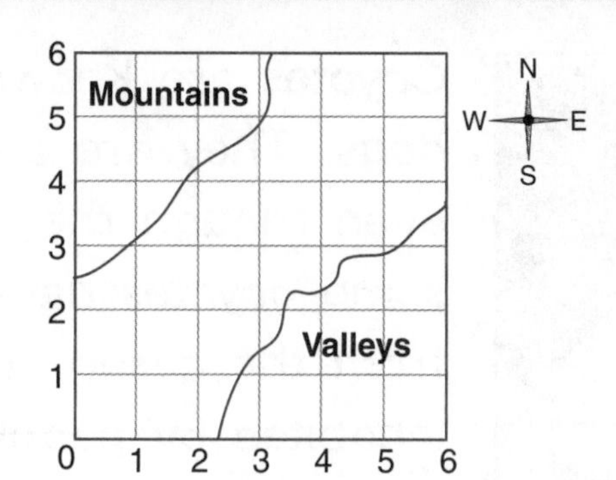

2 Scientists found coyote tracks leading from (1, 5) to (5, 1).

Looking at the grid, in what areas are these tracks located?

What do you know?

____

The tracks found at (1, 5) are in the __________. The tracks found at (5, 1) are in the __________.

3 One coyote is at (1, 4). Another coyote is at (4, 5). A rabbit is at (5, 3).

Name the coordinates of the coyote that is closer to the rabbit.

What do you know?

____

The coyote at __________ is closer to the rabbit.

4 A coyote sometimes teams up with a badger to hunt mice and other rodents. Scientists set up cameras at (2, 3) and (4, 3) to record this event. When the animals were halfway between these points, the camera photographed them.

When were the animals halfway between these points?

____

Explain your answer.

____

____

5 There is a coyote at (2, 4) and a badger at (4, 4). There are mice at (2, 1), (6, 3), and (3, 5). The coyote and the badger team up to hunt a mouse.

What are the coordinates of the mouse closest to both the coyote and the badger?

____

Explain your answer.

____

____

____

LESSON 9

Interpret Scale Drawings

Falling Rivers Niagara Falls is actually three falls. The Horseshoe Falls are in Canada. The Rainbow Falls are in New York State. The Rainbow Falls are made up of two waterfalls—the American Falls and the Bridal Veil Falls.

Niagara Falls

Niagara Falls is the only national landmark that is moving. As the water pours over the edge of the falls, it wears the rock away. This means the ledge is moving backwards. In about 25,000 years, the rock will be worn away all the way back to Lake Erie. The whole lake may pour over the falls, leaving a dry lake bed.

Estimate to decide what scale you should use.

Give It a Try

Make a scale drawing of the Rainbow Falls.

Rainbow Falls

Reminder

A **scale drawing** has the exact same shape as an object. But it is a different size. It may be larger or smaller than the object.

Whether the drawing is larger or smaller than the object, the proportions are always the same. **Proportions** are the relationships between the sizes of the different parts to each other and to the whole. For example, a car may be 3 times longer than it is tall. A scale drawing of that car will probably be much smaller than the actual car. But in the drawing the car will be 3 times longer than it is tall.

Step by Step

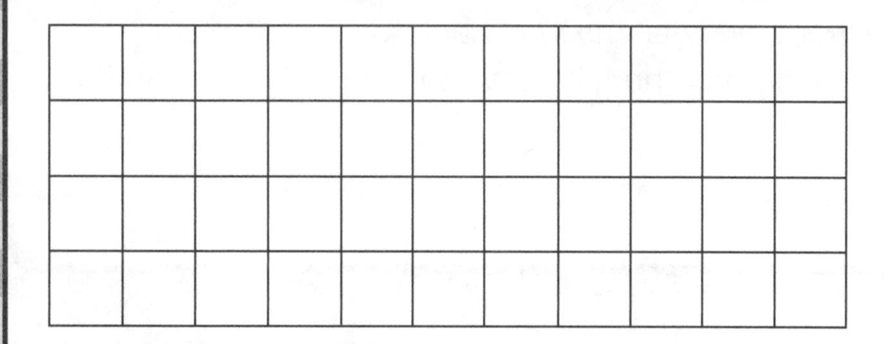

Ridge of Rainbow Falls is 330 meters wide and 60 meters from the water below.

1. Use a scale of 1 cm = 30 m. Each box on the grid measures 1 cm by 1 cm.
2. Start by drawing the rim of the falls.
   - **a.** How wide are the Rainbow Falls? ______
   - **b.** Find the number of 30-meter units in that width. ☐ ÷ 30 m = ______
   - **c.** Draw a line that many boxes wide across the top of the grid.
3. Follow the same steps to find how tall your drawing should be.
   - **a.** How high are the Rainbow Falls? ______
   - **b.** Find the number of 30-meter units in that height. ☐ ÷ 30 m = ______
   - **c.** Your drawing should be that many boxes tall.

How tall is your scale drawing? ______ cm How wide is it? ______ cm

Practice This

Use the scale drawing and a centimeter ruler to answer Questions 1–5.

1. How tall is the scale drawing of Yosemite Falls? ____________

Yosemite Falls
Scale: 1 cm = 115 m

2. How tall is the actual Yosemite Falls? ____________

3. How tall is the scale drawing of Angel Falls? ____________

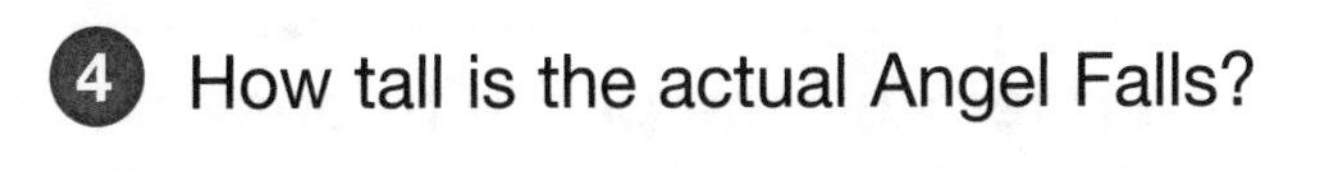

4. How tall is the actual Angel Falls? ____________

5. How much taller is the actual Angel Falls than the actual Yosemite Falls? ____________

Angel Falls
Scale: 1 cm = 115 m

Practice This

Use the scale drawing to answer Question 6.

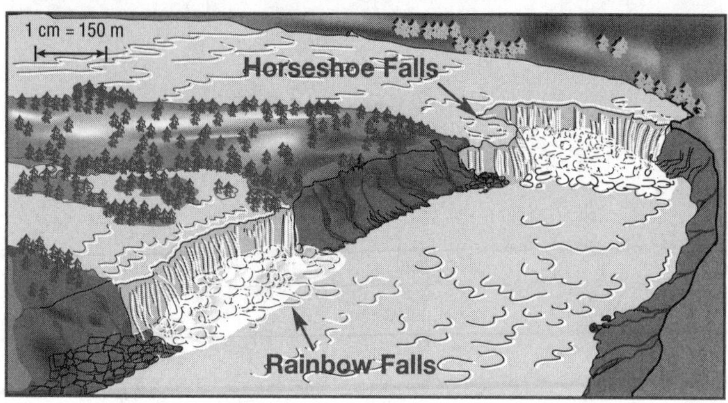

6. Explain how you would measure Horseshoe Falls and Rainbow Falls. How many meters is the larger falls greater than the smaller falls?

____

____

Horseshoe Falls are about 50 meters high and 650 meters wide.

Use a ruler and the photo to answer Questions 7–9.

7. If you were to make a scale drawing of Horseshoe Falls on the grid below, what scale would you use? ____________

8. Using that scale, how wide would your drawing be? How tall?

____

9. Make a scale drawing of Horseshoe Falls on the grid.

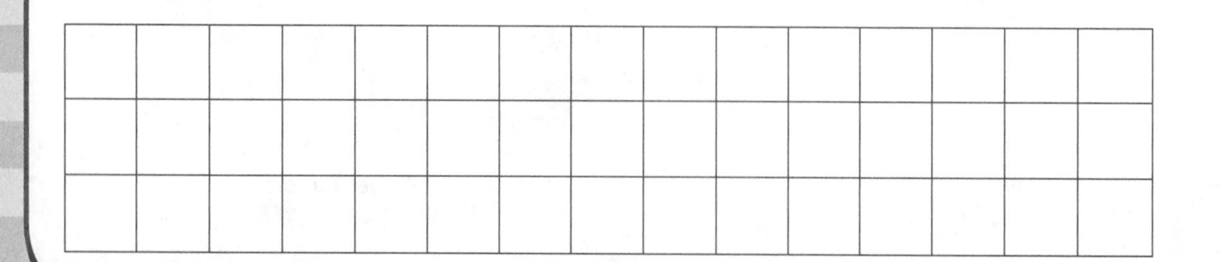

Problem Solving

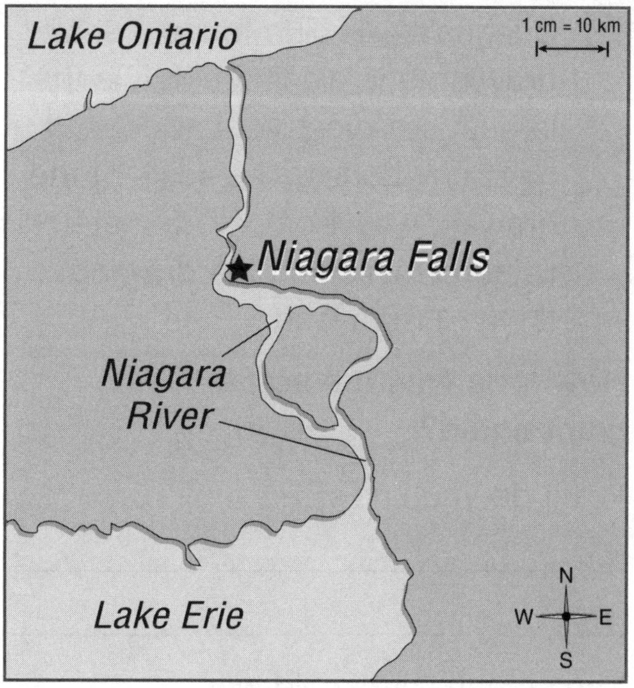

Solve.

1 Niagara Falls are 36 kilometers north of Lake Erie. Just north of the falls, the Niagara River spins through a large gorge, forming a whirlpool. The whirlpool is 40 kilometers north of Lake Erie.

Mark the point on the map where the whirlpool is.

a. Write what you know.

actual distance from Niagara Falls to Lake Erie: ______

actual distance from whirlpool to Lake Erie: ______

b. Find the scale of the drawing.

☐ cm = ☐ km

c. Calculate the distance from Niagara Falls to Lake Erie on the scale drawing:

☐ km ÷ ☐ = ☐ cm

Answer:

The whirlpool should be marked with a dot __________ cm north of Lake Erie.

Problem Solving Practice

2 Brianna's 4-H club found a scale drawing of a giant squid. It is the largest sea creature that doesn't have any bones. The scale of the drawing was 1 cm = 1.5 meters. Brianna measured the drawing. It was 11 cm long.

How long was the actual giant squid?

What do you know?

____

____

The actual giant squid was

__________ long.

3 Brianna found another drawing of a giant squid. The scale drawing of this squid was 1 cm = 2 m. The total length of the drawing was 9 centimeters. Without the feeding tentacles, the body alone measured 5.5 centimeters.

How long were the actual feeding tentacles?

What do you know?

____

____

The actual feeding tentacles were

__________ long.

4 A giant squid's eye was drawn to this size:

Scale: 1 mm = 1.5 cm

Use your ruler to find out how big the actual eye would be.

____

Explain how you got your answer.

____

____

____

____

5 Donna measured a painting of an octopus. It was 3.7 centimeters long. The scale said that 1 centimeter represented 1 meter.

Is this large octopus longer than the giant squid described in Question 3?

____

Explain how you got your answer.

____

____

____

____

____

LESSON 10

Interpret Data from Graphs

Fresh Water Imagine being on a raft in the middle of the ocean and not having anything to drink! Over 70% of our planet is covered by water. But only ocean creatures can use ocean water because it is salt water. Every other living thing must use fresh water.

About 3% of all water is fresh. But two thirds of that—2% of the total—is frozen in glaciers or ice caps, or is in the atmosphere as vapor. That means that less than 1% of the water on Earth is usable. And most of that is underground. River water is the easiest to use, but that offers only a tiny amount.

Imagine that every drop of water in the air turned into rain and fell. It would only cover the globe 1 inch deep. A heavy rainfall of 1 inch on one acre of land deposits only 27,000 gallons of water. That's about the amount of water in a swimming pool.

Give It a Try

In the United States, humans use about 38 billion gallons of water each day. A single family could use 600 gallons a day.

Which activity uses the largest amount of water?

Circle graphs show parts of a whole. They are used to make numerical comparisons.

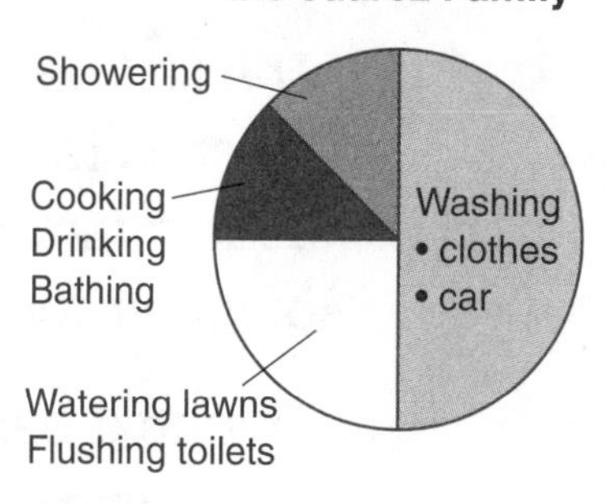

Bar graphs make numerical comparisons and also present exact values.

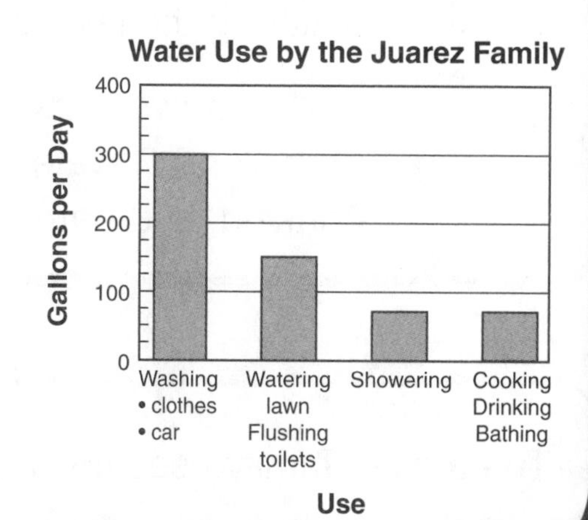

Approach 1: Use a Circle Graph to Show Parts of a Whole

STEP 1 Look at the graph and read the labels.

STEP 2 Compare the different sections of the graph.

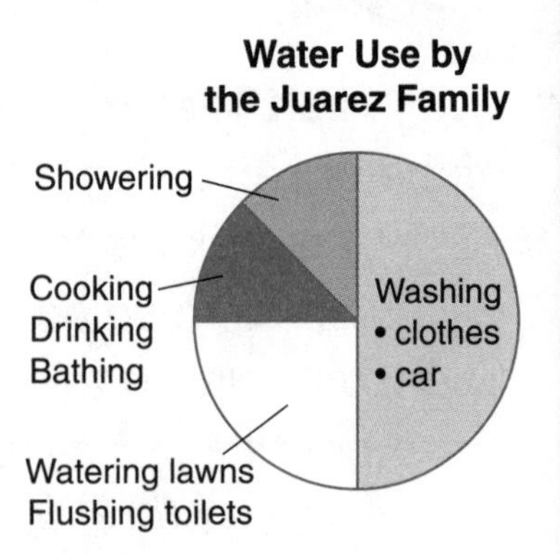

Half of the circle is labeled "Washing." This means that half of the water used by the family is for washing clothes and the car.

The next-largest section fills one quarter of the circle. One quarter of all the water used by the Juarez family is used for watering the lawn and flushing toilets.

The two smallest sections show equal amounts.

Approach 2: Use a Bar Graph to Find Actual Values

STEP 1 Look at the graph and read the labels.

STEP 2 Compare the different bars of the graph.

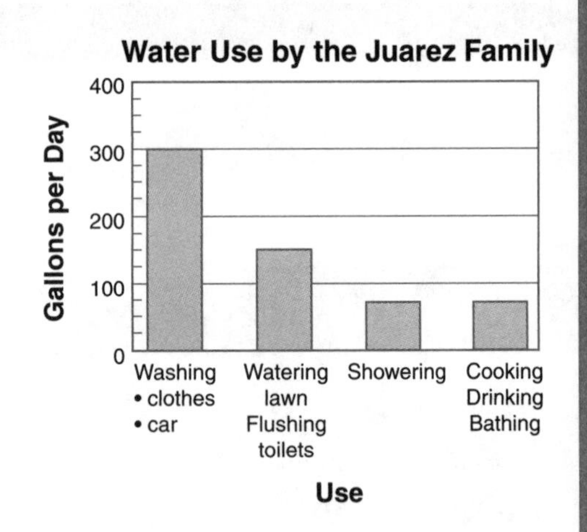

The first bar is labeled "Washing." It reaches to the line marked "300." The Juarez family uses 300 gallons of water for washing clothes and the car.

The next bar reaches the mark for "150." The Juarez family uses 150 gallons for watering the lawn and flushing the toilet.

The next two bars both reach the mark for "75." The Juarezes use 75 gallons of water for showering and another 75 gallons for cooking, drinking, and bathing.

The Juarez family uses the largest amount of water for ____________.

Practice This

Use the circle graph to answer these questions.

Water Use by the Juarez Family

Showering

Cooking
Drinking
Bathing

Washing
• clothes
• car

Watering lawns
Flushing toilets

1. Which section of the circle graph uses up more water than showering but less water than washing? ______________

2. Which uses, other than washing, make up half of the water the Juarez family uses? ______________

3. Which uses about the same amount of water as cooking, drinking, and bathing? ______________

4. Which uses about twice as much water as cooking, drinking, and bathing? ______________

5. Which uses about twice as much water as watering the lawn and flushing toilets? ______________

Use the bar graph to answer these questions.

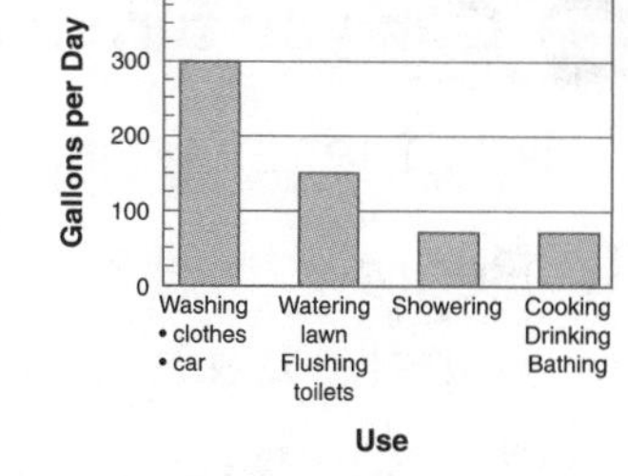

6. How many gallons do the Juarezes use for cooking, drinking, and bathing? ______________

7. For which other activity do the Juarezes use 75 gallons of water? ______________

8. How many gallons do the Juarezes use to water the lawn and flush the toilets? ______________

9. What is the Juarez family doing when they use twice as much water as cooking, drinking, and bathing? ______________

10. What is the Juarez family doing when they use twice as much water as watering the lawn and flushing toilets? ______________

Practice This

Use the graphs to answer these questions.

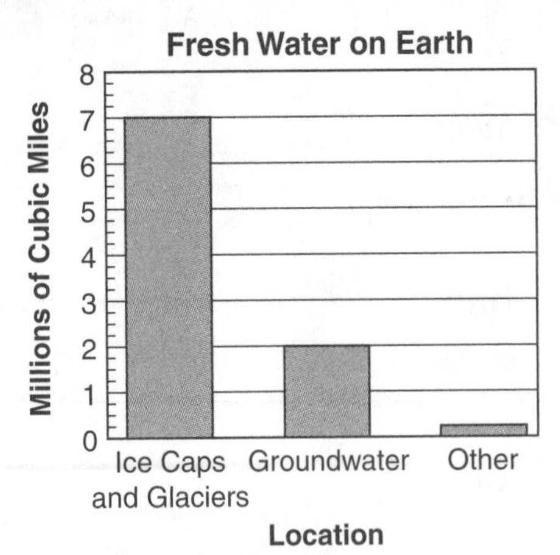

Fresh Water on Earth

Other

Groundwater

Ice Caps and Glaciers

11 Which graph would you use to find the actual amount of groundwater on the planet? Why?

____

____

How much would that amount be?

____

12 Which graph would you use to get an idea of the amount of ice on the planet compared with the amount of groundwater? Why?

____

____

____

13 Can you turn a bar graph into a circle graph?

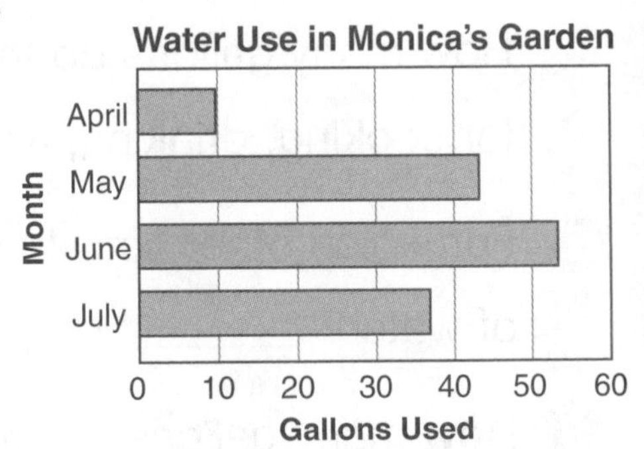

Follow these steps.

1. Redraw the bar graph on a separate piece of paper. Use a ruler to make sure your bars are the same length as the ones here.
2. Cut out each bar. Tape them together, end to end, to make a circle.

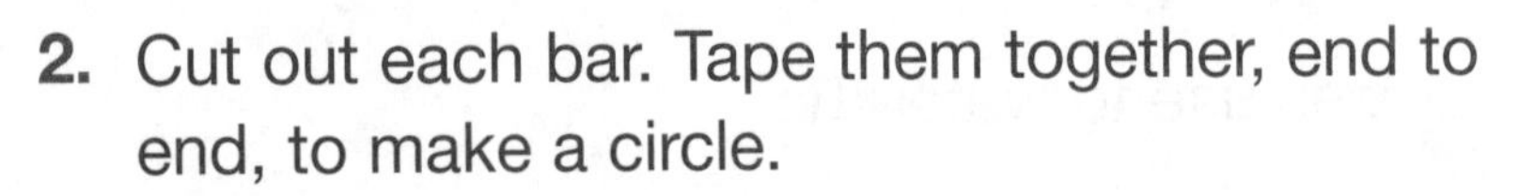

3. Place the circle on a piece of paper and trace it. Then mark the beginning and the end of each strip on the circle.

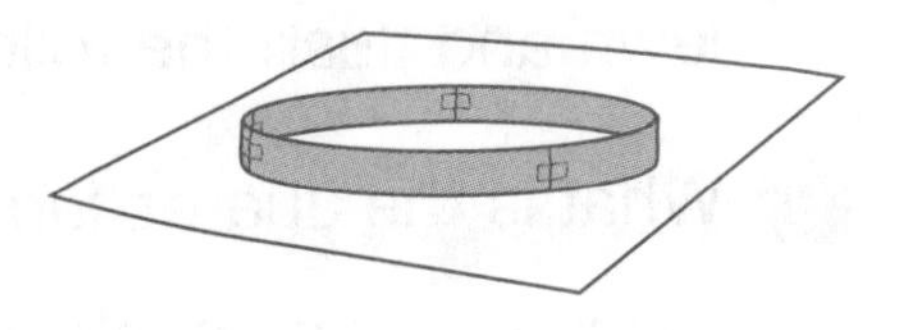

4. Draw lines from the marks you made to the center of the circle you drew.
5. Label each section.

Now you have your circle graph!

Problem Solving

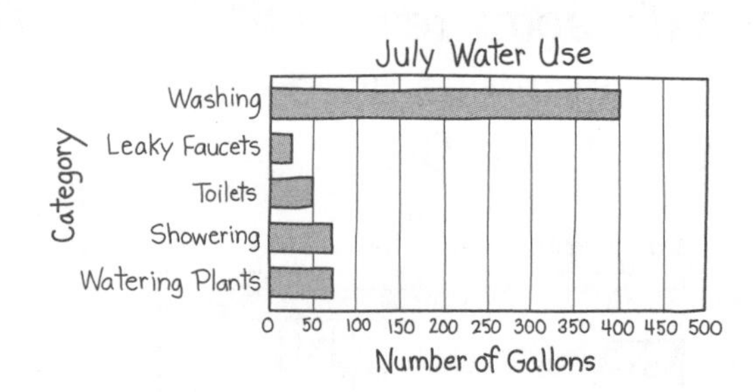

Solve.

1 Ian drew a circle graph showing his water use in June. He put the graph up in the kitchen. To save water, Ian installed toilets and shower heads that use less water. He shut off the faucet while he was shaving, brushing his teeth, or doing the dishes.

Ian used 800 gallons of water in June. What category of water use did he reduce the most in July?

a. Write what you know.

total water use in June: ____________

approximate amount used for washing in June: ____________

approximate amount used for watering in June: ____________

approximate amount used for showering in June: ____________

approximate amount used by toilets in June: ____________

approximate amount used by leaky faucets in June: ____________

b. Compare numbers.

amount washing use was reduced in July: ____________

amount watering use was reduced in July: ____________

amount showering use was reduced in July: ____________

amount toilet use was reduced in July: ____________

amount leaky faucet use was reduced in July: ____________

Answer:

Ian reduced his use of water for ____________ the most from June to July.

Problem Solving Practice

2 Victoria did some research into how water was used each day in the United States.

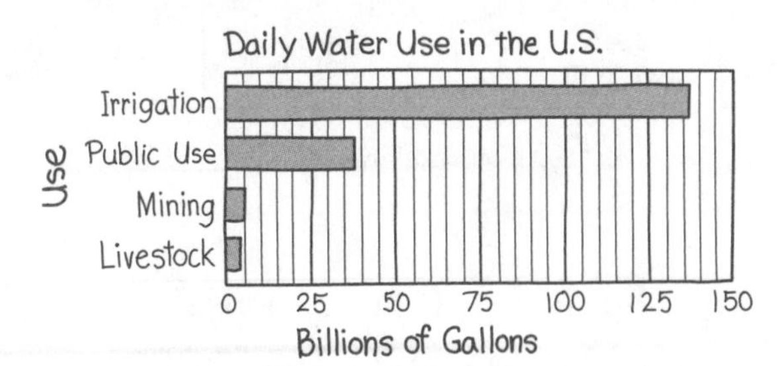

How does the amount of water used for irrigation compare to the other three usages of water?

What do you know?

____

____

The amount of water used for irrigation is __________ the amount used for the other three purposes.

3 Teresa was concerned about oil spills in the ocean. She created this circle graph to show the sources of oil pollution.

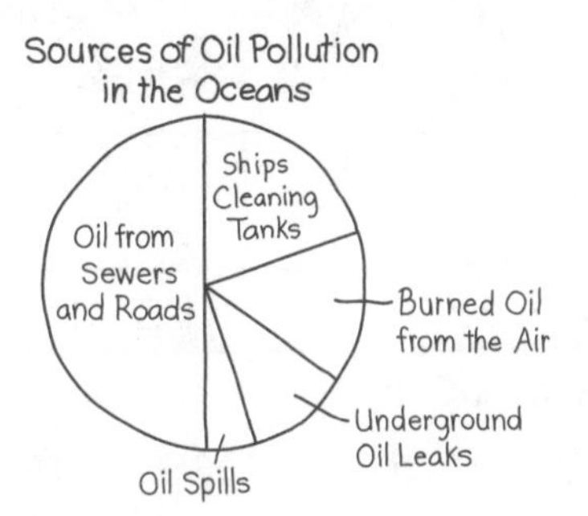

According to this graph, what is the third-largest source of oil pollution?

What do you know?

____

____

The third-largest source of oil pollution is ________________.

4 Would you use a bar graph or circle graph to show the exact monthly precipitation in each of the 50 states?

____

Explain your answer.

____

____

____

____

____

5 To show a comparison of the yearly precipitation in each of the 50 states, when you don't need to show exact values, would you use a bar graph or circle graph?

____

Explain your answer.

____

____

____

____

LESSON 11

Interpret Line Graphs

Our Growing Nation If you were to travel back in time, you would find a country that was very different from the one you live in. In the late 1700s, the United States reached only from the Atlantic Ocean to the Mississippi River. A little more than two million people lived in America at the end of the Revolutionary War. During the next fifty years, that number skyrocketed. Millions of people from all over the world immigrated to the new nation. By 1850, more than 23 million people were living in the United States!

Bald Eagle

The growing population brought changes to the natural environment. Animals like the bald eagle could not find safe nesting places. Food supply became limited, and many eagles were killed by people. The bald eagle was finally put on the endangered list of animals, and laws were passed to protect this living symbol of our nation.

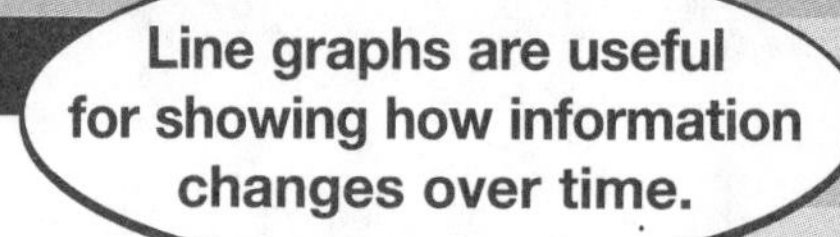

Give It a Try

The line graph shows the U.S. population from 1790 to 1850.

Between which two 10-year periods did the U.S. population increase the same amount?

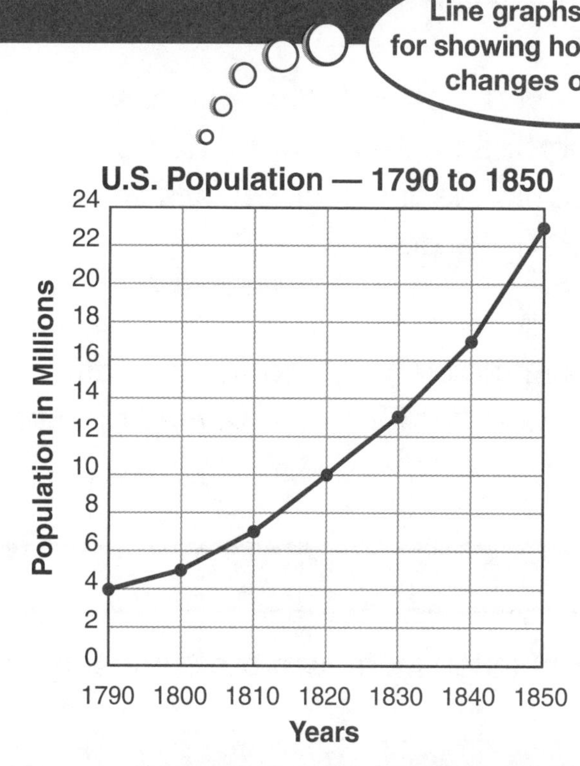

Reminder

- The vertical axis of a line graph is often divided into evenly spaced intervals. A number higher on the axis represents a greater amount than a number lower on the axis.
- The horizontal axis of a line graph often represents a change in time. As you move from left to right along the axis, time progresses.
- A line that slants upward shows numbers increasing over time. A line that slants downward shows numbers decreasing over time. A horizontal line shows a number remaining the same over time.

Step by Step

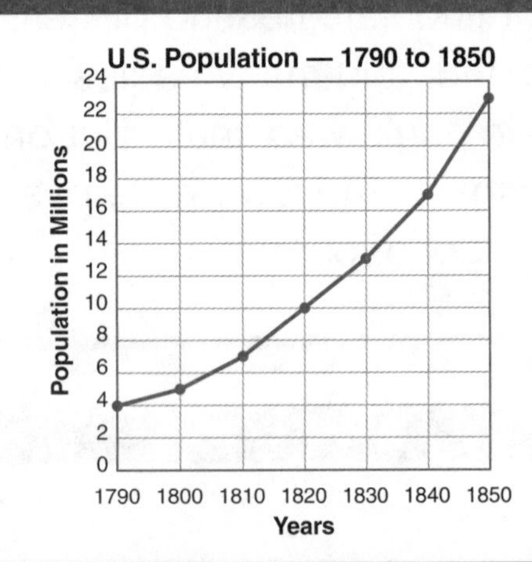

1. Read the vertical axis label on the graph. What does the axis represent?

   ____

2. Read the label on the horizontal axis. What does the axis represent?

   ____

3. Are you looking for an increase and/or a decrease in the data? Should the line segment(s) slant up and/or down?

   ____

4. Fill in the chart to find the increase in population for each ten-year period.

Ten-Year Period	Increase in Population (in millions)
1790–1800	1
1800–1810	2
1810–1820	3
1820–1830	
1830–1840	
1840–1850	

The population increased the same amount from ______ to ______ and from ______ to ______.

Practice This

Use the line graph to answer Questions 1–5.

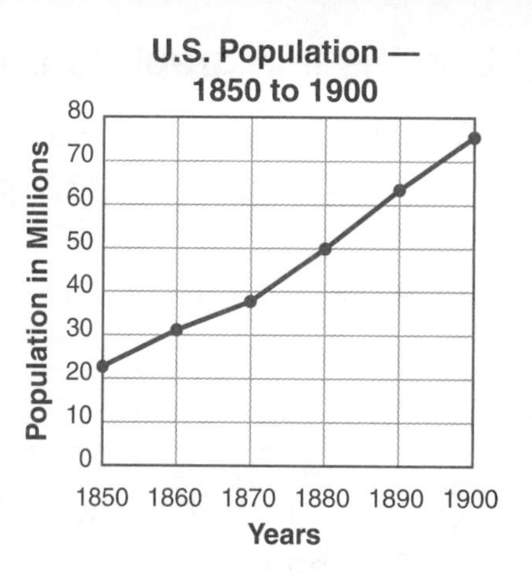

1. Read the label on the vertical axis. What does this axis represent? ________________
2. Read the label on the horizontal axis. What does this axis represent? ________________
3. In what year shown on the graph was the U.S. population the least? ________
4. In what year shown on the graph was the U.S. population the greatest? ________
5. What trend do you see in the data overall?

   ____

   ____

Use the line graph to answer Questions 6–9.

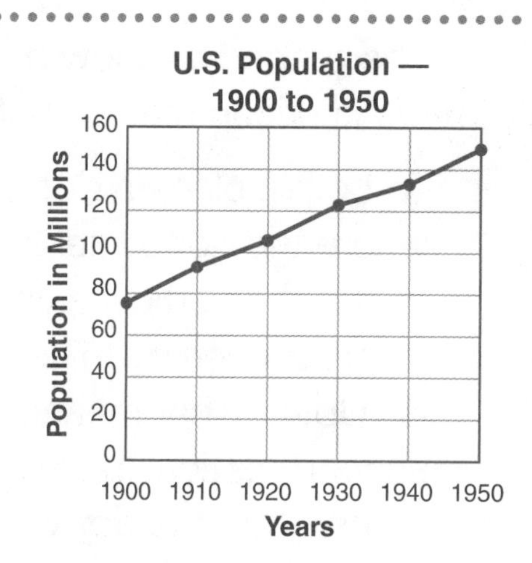

6. Read the label on the vertical axis. What does this axis represent?

   ____

7. Read the label on the horizontal axis. What does this axis represent?

   ____

8. About how many more people lived in the United States in 1950 than in 1900?

   ____

9. How did the population change between 1920 and 1930?

   ____

   ____

Practice This

Use the line graph to answer Questions 10 and 11.

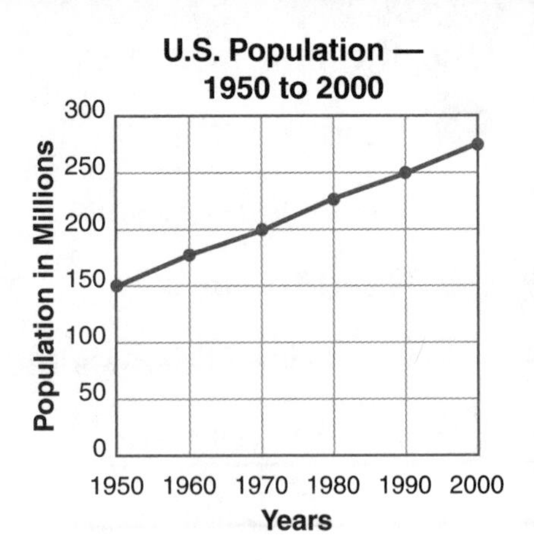

10. What trend can you see in the data from 1950 to 2000? Explain your answer.

____

____

____

11. Based on the data shown for the last 30 years, estimate the U.S. population in 2010. Explain how you arrived at your estimate.

____

____

____

12. You are going to draw a line graph. The graph will show how the number of American states changed over time.

To begin, place a dot on the graph where the horizontal line for "13" meets the vertical axis. Now look at the box below. The first instruction is "Up 4." That means the dot on the second vertical line will be four lines higher than the dot you just drew. Draw the second dot, then connect the two dots with a line. The second instruction is "Up 7." Continue until the graph is complete.

Up 4	Up 7	Up 7	Up 6	Up 7
Up 2	Up 2	Up 0	Up 2	

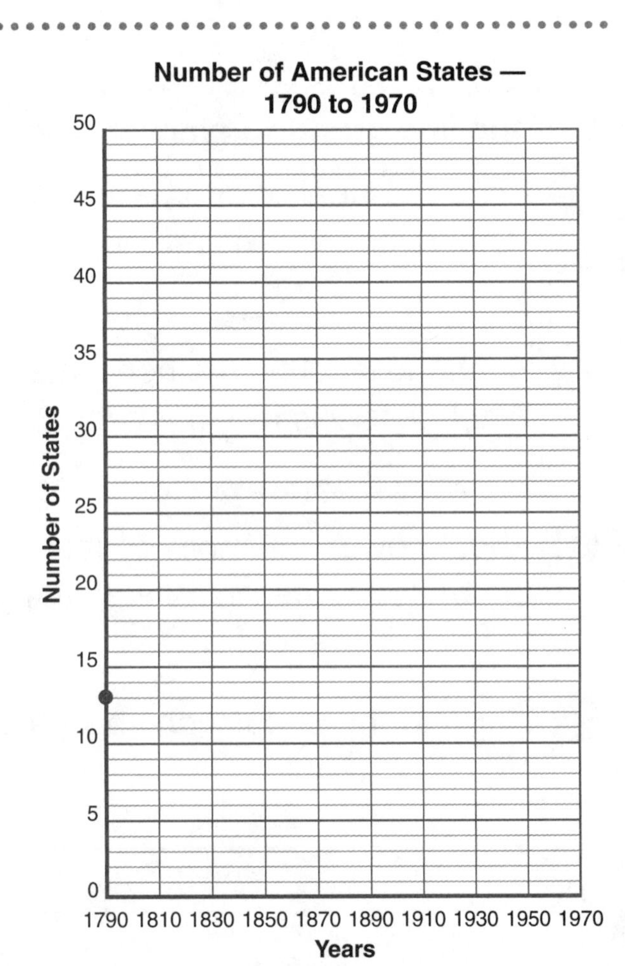

Problem Solving

DDT was a chemical used as a pesticide to get rid of insects that ate farmers' crops. But it also weakened the eggshells of bald eagles, causing their population to drop rapidly. Our government has since banned the use of DDT, and that has helped increase the population of bald eagles.

Solve.

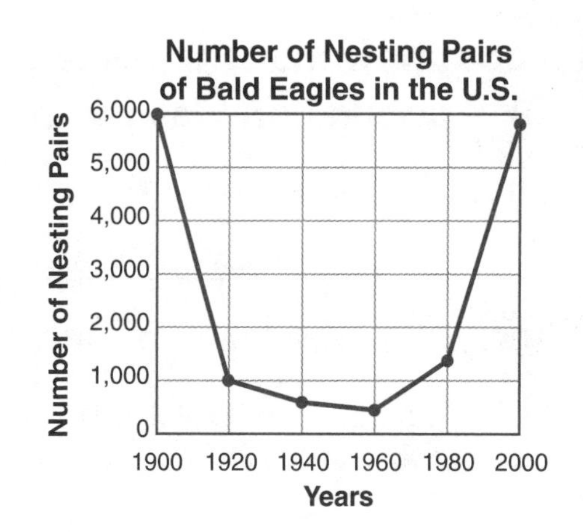

1. In the late 1700s, there were as many as 100,000 nesting pairs of bald eagles in the United States.

   What do you anticipate the population of bald eagles to be in 2010?

   a. When was the greatest decrease in population?

   ____

   b. When was the greatest increase in population?

   ____

Answer:

I anticipate the population of bald eagles to be __________ in 2010.

Problem Solving Practice

Use the line graph to answer Questions 2 and 3.

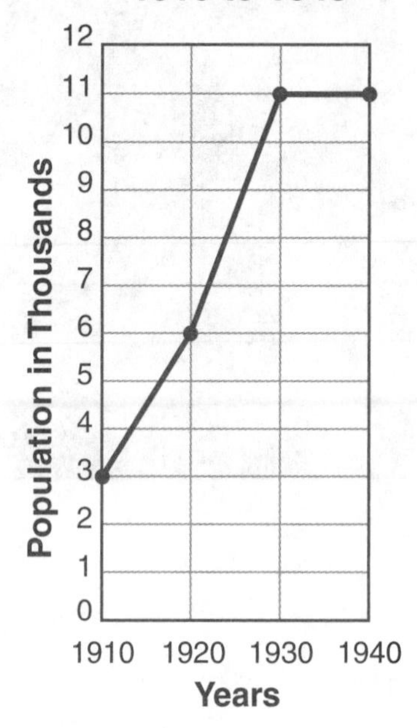

2. The line graph shows the population of Anaheim, California, from 1910 through 1940.

During which 10-year period did the population of Anaheim remain about the same?

What do you know?

____

Between ____________, the population of Anaheim, California, remained about the same.

3. In 2000, the population of Anaheim had grown to almost 330,000 people.

About how many times larger than the 1910 population was the 2000 population?

What do you know?

____

The 2000 population of Anaheim was

about ______ larger than the 1910 population.

4. Luke made a line graph to show how the population of his town changed from 1998 to 2002. He labeled the first horizontal line "0." He labeled the fourth horizontal line "15."

What labels should Luke place on the second and third lines?

____

Explain your answer.

____

____

5. Mrs. Dixon made a line graph showing how the population of her town changed from 1995 to 2001.

Is it possible to simply look at the line of the graph and name the year when her town had the least number of residents?

____

Why or why not?

____

____

Determine the Probability of an Event

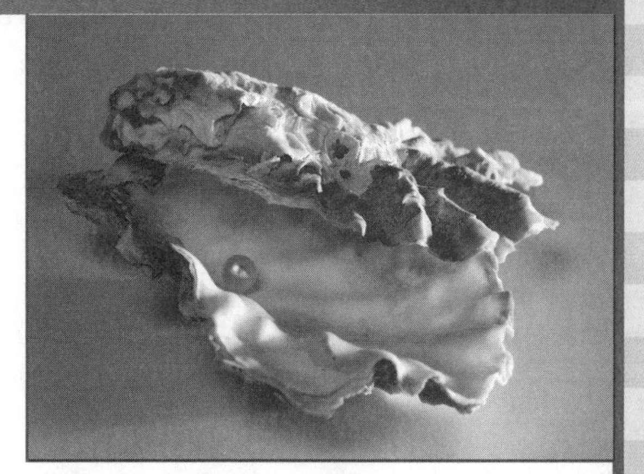

Treasures from the Sea Have you ever eaten an oyster? Did you know that the soft part of the animal inside the shell is more than a tasty treat? It is also a pearl-making machine!

Pearls are gems. They form when a solid particle becomes trapped inside the shell of certain kinds of oysters. The oyster releases fluids that coat the particle. Over time, the layers of fluids harden and form a pearl.

In the wild, only one in 10,000 oysters contains a pearl. But scientists have found a way to help this natural process occur. They place a small piece of shell inside a live oyster. That piece of shell starts the pearl-making process. Even so, only one out of twenty oysters will form a top-grade pearl. Four out of twenty will form pearls of medium quality.

Give It a Try

Scientists put shells inside 100 oysters.

How many top-grade pearls will likely form?

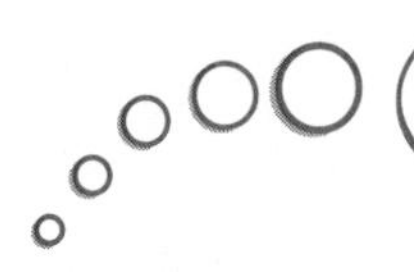

An *outcome* is a possible event.

- You can use logical reasoning to find the probability.
- Or, you can use equivalent fractions.

Approach 1: Use Logic

STEP 1 Find how many top-grade pearls you can expect from 20 oysters.

For every 20 oysters, you can expect 1 top-grade pearl.

STEP 2 Decide how many groups of 20 are in 100.

There are 5 groups of 20 in 100.

STEP 3 Determine how many pearls you can expect from 100 oysters.

$20 + 20 + 20 + 20 + 20 = 100$ oysters
$1 + 1 + 1 + 1 + 1 = 5$ top-grade pearls for 100 oysters

Approach 2: Use Equivalent Fractions

STEP 1 Write the probability of getting a top-grade pearl as a ratio, or fraction.

Probability of forming a top-grade pearl $= \frac{1}{20}$

STEP 2 Write the ratio you want to find.

Probability of top-grade pearls formed from 100 oysters $= \frac{x}{100}$

STEP 3 Change the first fraction to an equivalent fraction with a denominator of 100.

Here are two ways to find equivalent fractions:

a. Multiply the numerator and denominator by the same number.

$$\frac{1 \times 5}{20 \times 5} = \frac{5}{100}$$

$$\frac{1}{20} = \frac{5}{100}$$

b. Or, cross multiply to solve for x.

$$\frac{1}{20} = \frac{x}{100}$$

$$20x = 100$$

$$x = 5$$

If scientists put shells inside 100 oysters, ______ top-grade pearls will likely form.

Practice This

Use logic to solve the problems.

A gem company keeps a large number of oysters in vats. One vat contains 160 oysters. Workers put a small piece of shell inside each oyster in the vat.

1. **How many top-grade pearls could be expected from each vat of oysters?**

   Each group of 20 oysters produces 1 top-grade pearl.

   There are 8 groups of 20 in 160.

   So, ______ top-grade pearls could be expected from 160 oysters.

2. **How many medium-quality pearls could be expected from each vat?**

   Each group of 20 oysters produces 4 medium-quality pearls.

   So, for each group of 20, there are 4 times more medium-quality pearls than top-grade pearls.

   Therefore, $8 \times 4 =$ ______ medium-quality pearls.

Use equivalent fractions to solve the problems.

Another gem company has much larger vats. One vat contains 3,000 oysters. Workers put a small piece of shell inside each oyster in the vat.

3. **How many of the oysters could be expected to produce top-grade pearls?**

   $\frac{1}{20} = \frac{x}{3,000}$ $\quad$ $20x = 3,000$ $\quad$ $x = \square$

4. **How many of the oysters could be expected to produce medium-quality pearls?**

   There are 4 times more medium-quality pearls than top-grade pearls.

   So, $4 \times$ (number of top-grade pearls) $=$ ______ medium-quality pearls.

Practice This

Solve.

5 In one week, oyster gatherers collected 80,000 oysters from the wild.

How many of them might be expected to contain pearls?

Explain your answer.

Hint: Remember, oysters from the wild produce fewer pearls.

____

____

____

____

6 Imagine that the oyster gatherers inserted pieces of shell into all 80,000 oysters.

How many could be expected to produce top-grade pearls?

Explain your answer.

____

____

____

____

____

____

7 Draw a line from each ratio on the left to the words on the right that describe it. All ratios are in lowest terms.

$\frac{5}{7}$	Number of top-grade pearls to number of treated oysters
$\frac{1}{20}$	Consonants in the word *MOLLUSK* to the total number of letters in the word
$\frac{1}{5}$	Vowels in the word *PEARL* to the total number of letters in the word
$\frac{2}{5}$	Number of medium-quality pearls to number of treated oysters

Problem Solving

Pearls differ in shape, color, and luster (shine). Only the very best are given a rating of "perfect."

Solve.

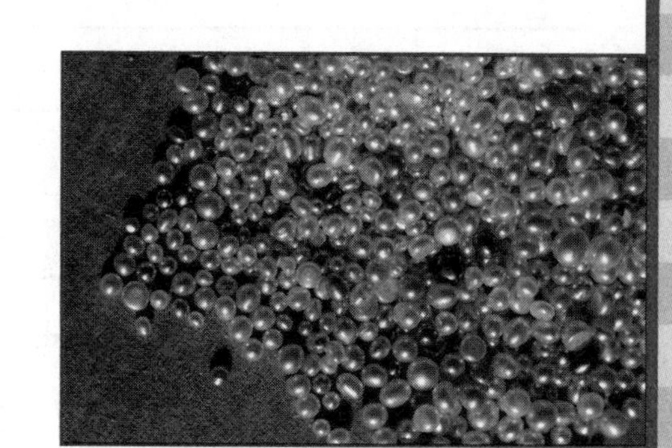

1 A pearl that is produced when a bit of shell is put inside an oyster is called a "cultured" pearl. Only 1 out of every 4 treated oysters produces cultured pearls. And only 5 out of every 100 cultured pearls are considered perfect.

How many oysters should a gem company treat in order to obtain 10 perfect pearls?

a. Write what you know.

Probability that a treated oyster will produce a cultured pearl: $\frac{\square}{\square}$

Probability that a cultured pearl will be perfect: 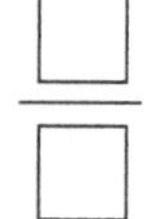

b. Set up equivalent fractions.

$\boldsymbol{x}$ = number of pearls that should be treated

$$\frac{5}{100} = \frac{10}{x}$$

$5x = \square$

$x = \square$ = number of pearls that should be treated

Answer:

The gem company should treat at least ______ oysters.

Problem Solving Practice

2 Workers at a gem company place a piece of shell inside every oyster in a vat. From this group of oysters, 124 medium-quality pearls are produced.

How many oysters were in the vat?

What do you know?

____

____

____

____

There were ______ oysters in the vat.

3 Another vat contains 2,000 oysters. Workers place a piece of shell inside each oyster in the vat.

How many perfect pearls could be expected from this vat?

What do you know?

____

____

____

____

______ perfect pearls could be expected from this vat.

4 Workers place a piece of shell inside each of 4,000 oysters.

How many oysters are NOT likely to produce a perfect pearl?

____

Explain your answer.

____

____

____

____

____

____

____

____

____

5 Workers place a piece of shell inside each of 200 oysters in another vat.

How many oysters are NOT likely to produce any pearls?

____

Explain your answer.

____

____

____

____

____

____

____

____

LESSON 13

Use Mean, Median, and Mode to Solve Problems

Shhh! The Animals Are Sleeping! If you own a cat or a dog, you're aware that these animals sleep part of each day. And, of course, you know how much you sleep each night. What you may not know is that almost all vertebrates (animals with backbones) need a daily period of rest. Sleep is a natural way of restoring the body's energy. Without daily sleep, the body cannot work properly.

The amount of time animals spend sleeping differs. Some animals, such as brown bats and pythons, spend as much as 20 hours a day sleeping. Other animals, such as elephants, sleep as little as 4 hours a day.

Give It a Try

The table on the right notes the average sleep time of some farm animals.

What are the *mean*, *median*, and *mode* of these data?

Average Hours of Daily Sleep for Various Farm Animals

Animal	Hours Asleep
cow	4
duck	11
horse	3
pig	8
sheep	4

- You can find the mean by evening out, then find the median and mode by arranging the data from greatest to least.
- Or, you can calculate the mean, then find the median and mode by arranging the data from least to greatest.

The *mean* is the average of the numbers in a data set. The *median* is the middle number in a data set. The *mode* is the number that occurs most often in a data set.

Approach 1: Find the Mean by Evening Out, Then Find the Median and Mode

STEP 1 Think of each number as a stack of blocks or counters. Subtract blocks from the largest stack. Add that many blocks to the smaller stacks.

Try Subtracting: 5

4	11	3	8	4
+ 1	− 5	+ 3	↓	+ 1
5	6	6	8	5

STEP 2 Repeat with the next largest stack.

Try Subtracting: 2

	5	6	6	8	5
	+ 1	↓	↓	− 2	+ 1
mean = 6	6	6	6	6	6

STEP 3 To find the median, arrange the data from greatest to least, then find the middle number.

11, 8, 4, 4, 3

median = 4

If there are two middle numbers, the median is equal to their mean.

STEP 4 To find the mode, find the number(s) that appear(s) most often.

11, 8, 4, 4, 3

mode = 4

If no number appears more often, there is no mode.

Approach 2: Calculate the Mean, Then Find the Median and Mode

STEP 1 To find the mean, start by finding the sum of the data set. **4 + 11 + 3 + 8 + 4 = 30**

STEP 2 Then divide the sum by the number of data in the set. **30 ÷ 5 = 6** **mean = 6**

STEP 3 To find the median, arrange the data from least to greatest. Find the middle number. **3, 4, 4, 8, 11** **median = 4**

STEP 4 To find the mode, find the number(s) that appear(s) most often. **3, 4, 4, 8, 11** **mode = 4**

The mean is _____. The median is _____. The mode is _____.

Practice This

Use the table to answer Questions 1–4.

1. What information does the table show?

____

____

____

Average Hours of Daily Sleep for Various Animals in the Wild	
Animal	**Hours Asleep**
cheetah	12
jaguar	11
lion	14
monkey	12
tiger	16

2. Use evening out to find the mean of the data. What is it? ______

3. What is the median of the data? ______

4. What is the mode of the data? ______

Use the table to answer Questions 5–8.

Average Hours of Daily Sleep for Various House Pets	
Animal	**Hours Asleep**
cat	13
dog	11
gerbil	13
guinea pig	9
guppy	7
hamster	14
rabbit	10

5. What information does the table show?

____

____

____

6. Calculate the mean of the data. What is it? ______

7. What is the median of the data? ______

8. What is the mode of the data? ______

Practice This

Use the table to answer Questions 9 and 10.

Average Hours of Daily Sleep for Various Animals in the Wild	
Animal	**Hours Asleep**
cheetah	12
jaguar	11
lion	14
monkey	12
tiger	16

9 Imagine that the following data were added to the table.

Animal	Hours Asleep
elephant	4
giraffe	1

How do you think that would affect the mean, median, and mode of the data set? Explain your thinking.

____

____

____

10 Find the mean, median, and mode for the data set with the numbers for elephant and giraffe.

____

Were your predictions correct? Why or why not?

____

____

Use the table to answer Questions 11 and 12.

11 Find the two animals that have a mean sleep time of 6.5 hours. Write the name of the one with the shorter sleep time in the 1st sentence. Write the name of the one with the longer sleep time in the 2nd sentence.

12 Find the median of the data set. Write the name of that animal in the last sentence.

Average Hours of Daily Sleep for Various Animals in the Wild	
Animal	**Hours Asleep**
dolphin	10
duck	12
giraffe	1

A __________ sleeps standing up.

A __________ can sleep with one eye open and one eye shut.

Only half of a __________'s brain sleeps at a time.

Problem Solving

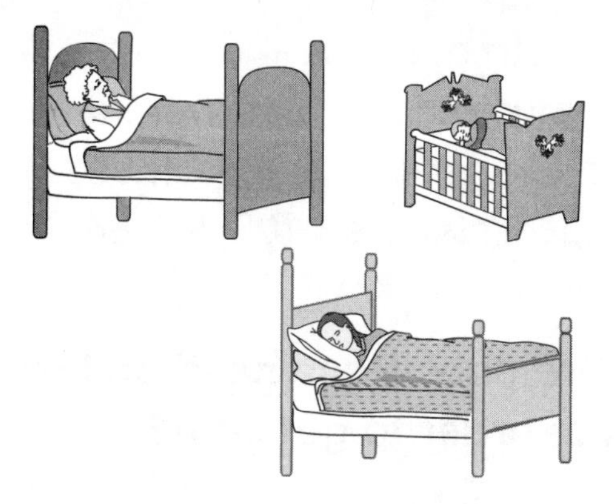

Human babies sleep as much as 16 hours a day. Adults usually sleep about 8 hours a night. But that drops to about $5\frac{1}{2}$ hours as people get older.

Solve.

1 Rosa took a survey for her science class. She asked 12 classmates how many hours they slept the previous Saturday night. Their responses are listed below.

10 8 9 10 9 8 10 7 10 9 10 8

Rosa says that the mean sleep time is 9 hours. Do you agree? Why or why not?

a. Write what you know.

to find the mean: __________

number of classmates asked: ☐

b. Compare answers.

mean Rosa found: ☐

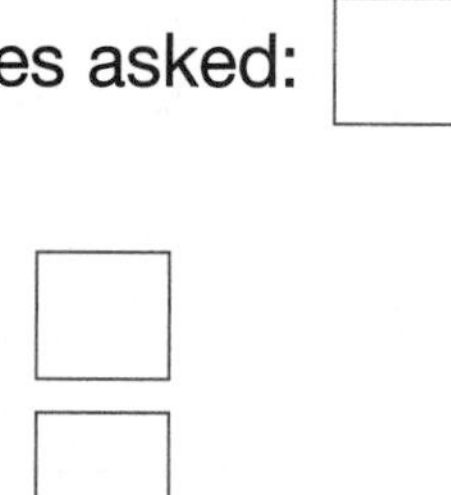

mean you found: ☐

Answer:

I ______ that the mean sleep time is 9 hours because the mean sleep time I found is ______ hours.

Problem Solving Practice

2 Brian is in Rosa's science class. He took his own survey of 12 other classmates. Their responses are listed below.

7 10 9 7 9 8 6 7 7 9 8 9

Brian says the data set has no mode. Do you agree with him? Why or why not?

What do you know?

____

____

I __________ with Brian because

____

______________________________.

3 In order to get an A in Science, Rosa must have a test average of 92. On her first four science tests, Rosa scored 100, 92, 84, and 95.

What score does Rosa need on her fifth test in order to get an A?

What do you know?

____

____

____

____

In order to get an A, Rosa must score at least ____ on the fifth test.

4 Brian wants to find his median test score. On his first four science tests, he scored 75, 85, 85, and 87. Brian says he does not have to do any calculations to find the median.

Do you agree or disagree with him?

____

Explain your answer.

____

____

____

____

____

5 Can you think of any cases in which you would not have to do calculations in order to find a mean? Give two examples, and explain why you would not have to do any calculations.

____

____

____

____

____

____

____

____

LESSON 14

Create a Chart and Make a List

Gregor's Genetics In 1856, a monk named Gregor Mendel began experimenting with plants in the gardens at the monastery. In seven years, he raised 28,000 pea plants. He studied the traits, or characteristics, of the pea plants. He carefully recorded the traits in the adult plants that produced certain traits in their offspring. He showed how the size, or color, or other traits of a living thing were passed from parent to offspring.

In his experiments, Mendel proved that a short pea plant and a tall pea plant would produce seeds that grew only tall plants in the first generation. However, in the next generation, $\frac{3}{4}$ of the plants produced from those seeds would be tall, and $\frac{1}{4}$ of the plants would be short. Some traits can skip a generation.

Give It a Try

Mendel paired a tall plant with a short plant and produced 4 tall plants.

He then paired these 4 as 2 sets of parents. In the second generation, 6 were tall and 2 were short.

How many plants were short or tall in the third generation?

Every 2 plants paired creates 4 new plants in the next generation.

Generation 1:

___ tall plant + ___ short plant =

___ tall plants

Generation 2:

___ plants = ___ pairs of plants =

___ tall plants and ___ short plants

Generation 3:

___ plants = ___ pairs of plants =

___ tall plants and ___ short plants

- You can create a chart showing generations to solve the problem.
- Or, you can make a list to solve the problem.

Approach 1: Create a Chart

A chart is a way of showing the offspring of two parents. Each row is a generation. Fill in the results of each pairing. Remember a Tall plant and a Short plant make 4 Tall plants. The offspring of 2 Tall plants are 3 Tall plants and 1 Short plant. Write T for Tall and S for Short.

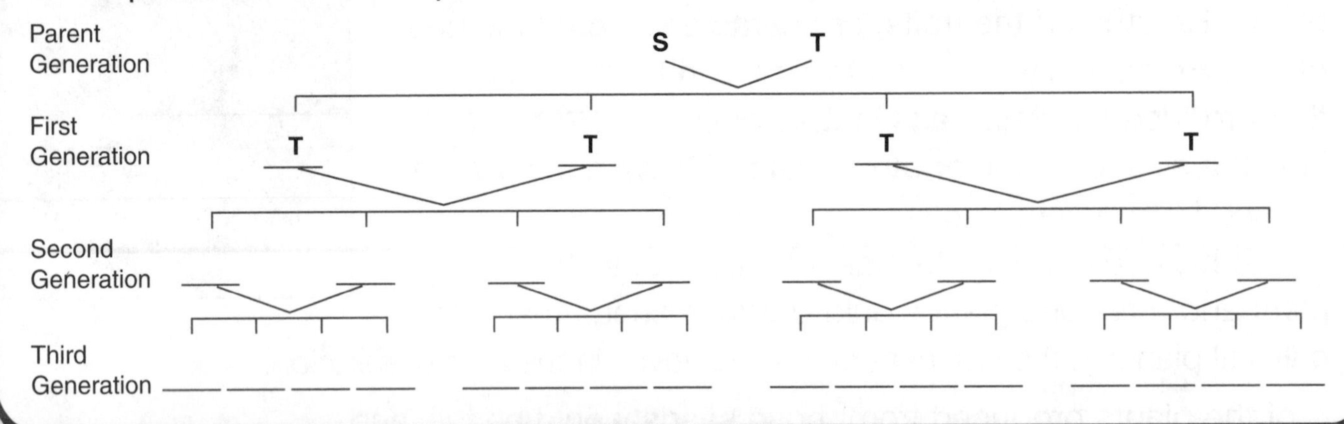

Approach 2: Make a List

STEP 1 Make a list of possible combinations. ST is a pairing of a Short and a Tall plant. TT is a pairing of two Tall plants.

The offspring of ST is 4T.
This First Generation forms 2 pairs: TT and TT.
The offspring of the First Generation is the Second Generation.
The Second Generation is 3T, 1S and 3T, 1S.

The Second Generation forms 4 pairs: TT, ST and TT, ST.
The offspring of the Second Generation is the Third Generation.
The Third Generation is 3T, 1S, 4T and 3T, 1S, 4T.

STEP 2 List the results from each generation.

Parent Generation: ST
First Generation: 4T
Second Generation: 6T, 2S
Third Generation: 14T, 2S

So, ___ Tall and ___ Short plants make up the Third Generation.

Practice This

Solve.

1. Mendel also experimented with the color of the pea. He paired 2 yellow pea plants. They produced 3 plants with yellow peas and 1 plant with green peas. When he paired a plant with yellow peas and a plant with green peas, he got 4 plants with yellow peas. How many plants had yellow or green peas in the Third Generation?

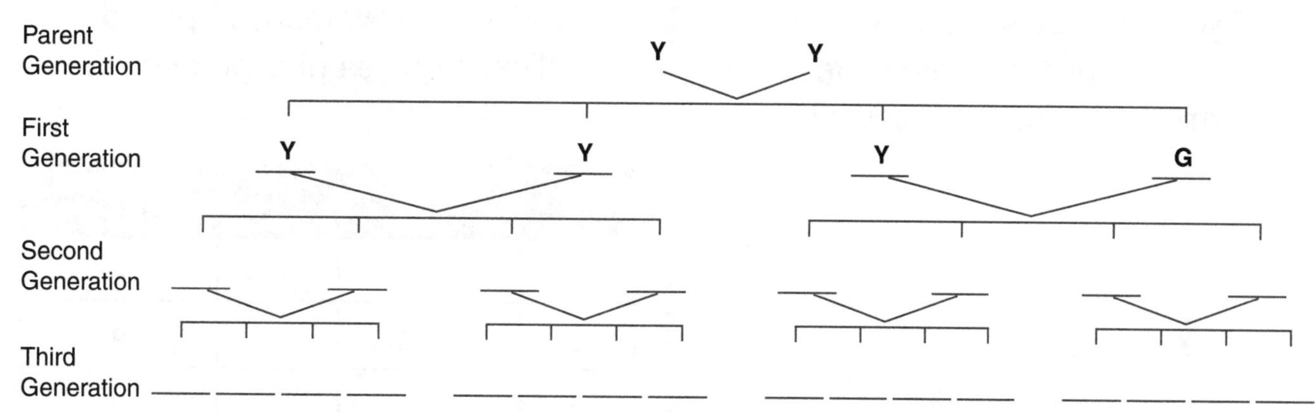

In the Third Generation, ___ plants had yellow peas and ___ plants had green peas.

2. Ula's hamsters always had one more male than female in their litters. The first litter had 3 males. The next litter had 5 females. The third litter had 5 males. How many hamster pups were produced by Ula's hamsters in 3 litters?

	Males (F + 1)	Females (F)	Total
Litter 1			
Litter 2			
Litter 3			

___ + ___ + ___ = ___

Ula's hamsters produced ___ hamsters in 3 litters.

Practice This

Solve.

3 Make a list to help you answer the question. A male and a female horse produced 3 offspring. One of their offspring was female and she had 5 babies in her life. Two were males. How many males and females total were there in this family, counting the parents?

There were ___ males and ___ females in this family.

4 Use a chart to help you answer the question. Nicky's guinea pigs had a litter of 4 pups. The total for each of the next 3 litters increases 1 more than the total for the litter before it. How many pups did Nicky's guinea pigs produce in all 4 litters?

Litter	Number in Litter	Total	Cumulative Total
1	4	4	4
2	4 + 1		9
3			15
4			

A total of ___ pups were produced in 4 litters.

5 Amy and Bill have 4 children named Carol, David, Emily, and Fred. David has 4 children and Carol has 2 boys and a girl. Fred has no children. Amy and Bill have 9 grandchildren. How many children does Emily have?

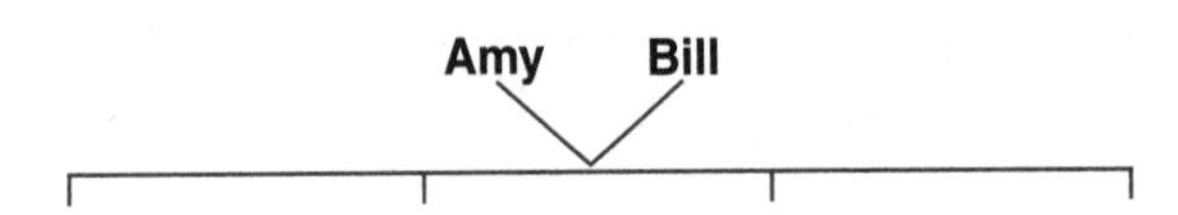

Problem Solving

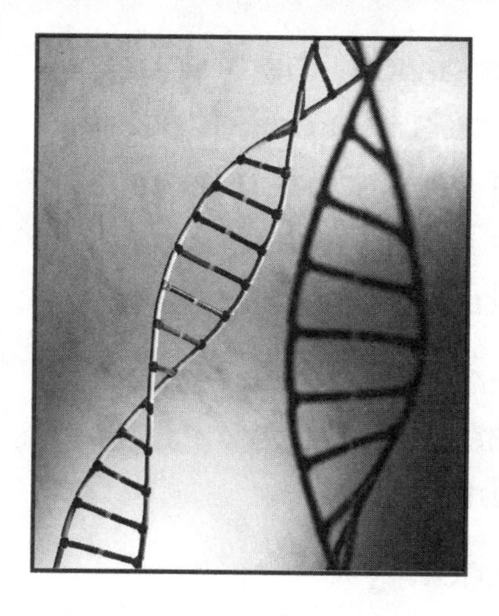

After Gregor Mendel's experiments, scientists worked to discover how cells produce new cells with the same traits. They discovered the DNA molecule. DNA is a complicated structure within every cell. Chemicals called guanine, cytosine, adenine, and thymine are linked in a special order. The molecules form a structure like a twisted ladder. Adenine (A) only connects to thymine (T) as AT or TA. Guanine (G) only attaches to cytosine (C) as GC or CG. When DNA duplicates itself, it splits down the middle of these connections. Then each side of the "ladder" connects to other chemical molecules in the same order.

DNA Molecule	
Original Side	New Side
C	
T	
A	
A	
G	
A	
T	
C	
G	
A	
T	
C	
G	
G	
A	
T	
C	

Solve.

1 If one side of a DNA molecule is CTAAGATCGATCGGATC, what molecules would connect to the chain to complete the DNA molecule?

a. You can create a chart to make the connections.

Adenine only connects to ___________.

Guanine only connects to ___________.

b. On the new side of the DNA molecule, which are there most of: adenine, thymine, guanine, or cytosine? ___________

Answer:

On the new side of the DNA molecule, there are more ___________.

Problem Solving Practice

2 Gregor Mendel had 6 plots in one of his gardens. The peas have to be across from the lettuce. The carrots have to be between the beans and the peas. The corn has to be opposite the carrots.

What would be across from the flowers?

What do you know?

____

____

__________ would be across from the flowers.

3 When cells divide, the number of chromosomes in a cell doubles, then splits in half. Each new half then splits in half again. A frog body cell has 26 chromosomes.

How many chromosomes are in the frog cell after the cell finishes dividing?

What do you know?

____

____

Each frog cell has ___ chromosomes after it finishes dividing.

4 A strand of DNA contains one of each pair of chemicals. It follows alphabetical order of the first letter. Each time it duplicates itself it adds one pair of molecules, but in reverse. It alternates placing the new combination at the front and back.

Switch the letters and move them to the front. **Switch the letters and move them to the back.**

AT, CG, GC, TA

Repeat #1: TA, AT, CG, GC, TA

Repeat #2: TA, AT, CG, GC, TA, GC

What would the DNA pattern be after the fourth duplication?

____

Explain your answer.

____

____

5 Two bean plants create 4 bean plants. These 4 bean plants create 8 bean plants.

Generation	Number of Plants	Total
1	2	2
2	2^2	4
3	2^3	8

How many bean plants would be in the sixth generation?

____

Explain your answer.

____

____

____

____

LESSON 15

Make a Table and Use Logic

I Dig Fossils Fossils are the remains of animals and plants that lived a long time ago. Some fossils are the actual bodies of animals and plants. The remains were protected in ice or in hardened tree sap. Rivers or the wind can uncover fossil bones so they are sticking out of the ground.

Fossils are clues to what life was like on Earth millions of years ago. Fossil eggs show that dinosaurs sat on nests like birds. Dinosaurs left tracks in mud and then the mud turned to stone. These tracks show that some dinosaurs traveled in herds. Even a tiny tooth can tell scientists how that animal lived.

Almost every place on Earth has fossils of some kind. A 12-year-old girl discovered the skin of a Tyrannosaurus Rex. A 3-year-old found a dinosaur egg. Some places have lots of fossils.

Give It a Try

Scientists were digging up fossils at two different sites. They dug 38 fossils at both Site A and B the first day. The second day they found 17 fossils at Site B and 49 at Site A. On Day 3 they found 9 more at Site B than they did at Site A.

If the total number of fossils found at Site A was 115, what was the total found at Site B?

Use the totals given to find amounts you don't know.

Site A:

Day 1 total + Day 2 total + ☐ = 115

Site B:

Day 1 total + Day 2 total +
Site A Day 3 total + 9 = Total Fossils Found

- You can make a table to solve the problem.
- Or, you can use logic to solve the problem.

Approach 1: Make a Table

STEP 1 Create a table with rows for each site. Put in columns for each day and the total known. Fill in the information given in the problem. Let A equal the number of fossils found at Site A on Day 3. Let B equal the total number of fossils found on all three days at Site B.

	Day 1	Day 2	Day 3	Total
Site A	38	49	A	115
Site B	38	17	A + 9	B

STEP 2 Add the Day 1 and Day 2 total from Site A. $38 + 49 = 87$
Subtract Day 1 and Day 2 Total from Site A total. $115 - 87 = 28$
The total for Day 3 at Site A is 28.

Find Day 3 Total for Site B by adding. $28 + 9 = 37$
Add Day 1 + 2 + 3 totals for Site B. $38 + 17 + 37 = 92$

Approach 2: Use Logic

Notice that on Day 2, 32 ($49 - 17$) more fossils were found at Site A than at Site B. On Day 3, only 9 more fossils were found at Site B than at Site A. So, the total for Site B must be less than the total for Site A.

Since the same number of fossils were found at each site on Day 1, subtract 38 from the total. ($115 - 38 = 77$) The total for Day 2 and Day 3 at Site A must equal 77.

Subtract to find the total for Day 3 at Site A. ($77 - 49 = 28$)

Use the total for Day 3 at Site A to find the total for Day 3 at Site B. ($28 + 9 = 37$)

Now add all the figures to find the total at Site B. ($38 + 17 + 37 = 92$)

The total number of fossils found at Site B was ______.

Practice This

Solve using a table.

1. There were many different types of dinosaurs. One day 7 students were digging at a Sauropod site. Four more students than this were at a Plesiosaur site. The next day the crew was doubled at the Plesiosaur site. Six more students were needed at the Sauropod site than the Plesiosaur site on Day 2. The total number of students working at the Sauropod site turned out to be 47. The total working at the Plesiosaur site was 52. How many students worked at each of these sites on Day 3?

	Day 1	Day 2	Day 3	Total
Sauropod				
Plesiosaur				

The total number of students at the Sauropod site on Day 3 was ______.

The total number of students at the Plesiosaur site on Day 3 was ______.

Solve using logic.

2. Look back at the table above. There were twice the number of students at the Theropod site each day as were at the Sauropod and Plesiosaur sites combined. How many students were at the Theropod site each day? What was the total number of students at the Theropod site?

Day 1: (Sauropod ______ + Plesiosaur ______) × 2 = ______

Day 2: (Sauropod ______ + Plesiosaur ______) × 2 = ______

Day 3: (Sauropod ______ + Plesiosaur ______) × 2 = ______

Use the totals to find the total number of students working at the Theropod site.

______ + ______ + ______ = ______

The total number of students at the Theropod site was ______.

Practice This

Solve with a table or use logic.

3 Donna and Herve looked for dinosaur teeth. At different sites, they kept records of what they found. At Site 1, Donna found 21 teeth and Herve found 4 fewer teeth than Donna. At Site 2, Herve found 8 more than he found at Site 1. Donna found 5 fewer than Herve at Site 2. How many teeth did they find altogether?

Herve's Total: ______

Donna's Total : ______

4 Heather and Jim looked for dinosaur teeth. Heather found 3 fewer teeth than Jim on Sunday. On Sunday, Jim found 2 more teeth than he found on Saturday. Heather found 11 teeth on Saturday. Jim found 12 teeth on Sunday. Who found more teeth?

	Saturday	Sunday	Total
Heather			
Jim			

__________ found more teeth

5 After a fossil is discovered, it is carefully packed up and moved to a lab. Use the table to help a scientist schedule when to bring different kinds of fossils to the lab. Write your possibilities in pencil. Erase and move them if you need to change. Only one type of fossil can be moved each day.

Type of Fossil	Monday	Tuesday	Wednesday	Thursday	Friday
Tyrannosaurus Rex					
Velociraptor					
Triceratops					
Allosaurus					
Diplodocus					

The Tyrannosaurus Rex should be moved one day after the Velociraptor.

The Diplodocus has to be moved earlier in the week than the Tyrannosaurus Rex, but it must follow the Allosaurus.

The Triceratops has to be moved on Wednesday.

Problem Solving

Hagerman Fossil Beds National Monument in Idaho is over 4,000 acres and has over 12,000 visitors a year. Fossil Butte National Monument in Wyoming is twice the size of Hagerman and has 1.6 times as many visitors. John Day Fossil Beds National Monument in Oregon is almost twice the size of Fossil Butte and has more than 5 times as many visitors.

Solve.

1 How many acres is John Day Fossil Beds National Monument? How many people visit it each year?

National Monument	Acres	Visitors
Hagerman Fossil Beds	4,000	12,000
Fossil Butte		
John Day Fossil Beds		

a. Write what you know.

Hagerman Fossil Beds: acres: ______ visitors: ______

b. You can make a table and use logic.

Fossil Butte is twice the size of Hagerman: ______ × ______ = ______

Fossil Butte has 1.6 times as many visitors as Hagerman:

______ × ______ = ______

John Day Fossil Beds is almost twice the size of Fossil Butte:

______ × ______ = ______

John Day Fossil Beds has 5 times as many visitors:

______ × ______ = ______

John Day Fossil Beds

Answer:

John Day Fossil Beds National Monument is almost ______ acres and has more than ______ visitors each year.

Problem Solving Practice

A family can visit a dinosaur dig site for $700 a day for 3 days. You stay at 3 different hotels. The hotel for Day 3 costs half the total per day. One of the other two hotels costs $25 more, the other hotel costs $100 more. Food on Day 1 and 3 is $125 and the total cost of food is $450. Other costs on Day 1 and 2 are the same as food on Day 3.

	Hotel	Food	Other	Total
Day 1				$700
Day 2				$700
Day 3	$350			$700

2. **How much would a family spend on hotels for 3 days?**

What do you know?

____

____

_______ would be the cost of hotels for all 3 days.

3. **How much would a family save if they didn't pay the Day 2 amount for food?**

What do you know?

____

____

They would save _______ if they didn't pay the Day 2 amount for food.

4. On the third day of their vacation, the Quinn family spent $130 from their Other costs on souvenirs from the dig sites.

How much money would they have left for Other costs on Day 3?

____

Explain your answer.

____

____

5. There are many expenses while traveling.

What is the greatest expense in this 3-day vacation plan?

____

Explain your answer.

____

____

____

Fill in the circle next to the correct answer.

For short response problems, write the answer in the space provided.

1. Mark wants to compare the decimals. Should he use >, <, or =?

0.2 ☐ **0.08**

2. Amy was asked to compare the decimals. What symbol should she write?

5.03 ☐ **4.99**

Ⓐ >   Ⓑ <   Ⓒ =

3. Show Kathy how to add the fractions.

$\frac{4}{7} + \frac{2}{7} =$ ☐

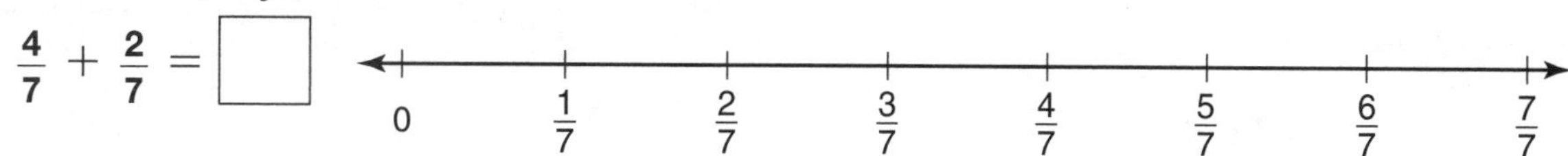

4. Chen knows how to subtract fractions. Help him find the correct answer.

$\frac{7}{8} - \frac{2}{8} =$ ☐

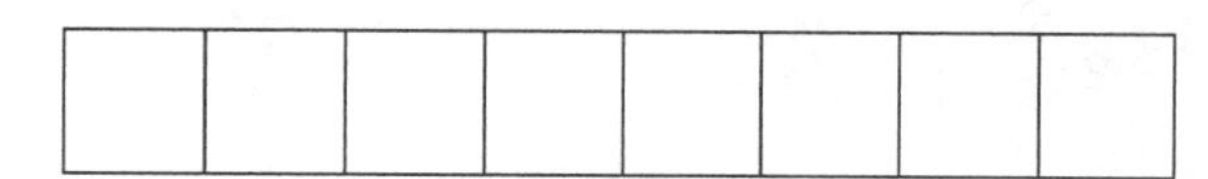

Ⓐ $\frac{9}{8}$ Ⓑ $\frac{5}{8}$ Ⓒ $\frac{4}{8}$ Ⓓ $\frac{3}{8}$

5 Dana wants to subtract the mixed numbers. Show her how to find the correct answer.

$3\frac{4}{5} - 1\frac{1}{5} = \square$

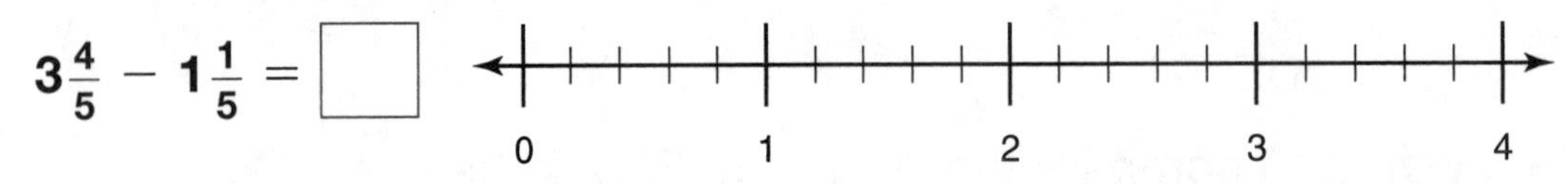

6 Abe was asked to find the sum of these mixed numbers. Which answer is the correct sum?

$4\frac{5}{9} + 2\frac{3}{9} = \square$

Ⓐ $2\frac{2}{9}$ Ⓑ $6\frac{2}{9}$ Ⓒ $6\frac{8}{9}$ Ⓓ $6\frac{8}{18}$

7 Megan knows how to write the equivalent fraction for a percent. Use the grid to help you write the equivalent fraction.

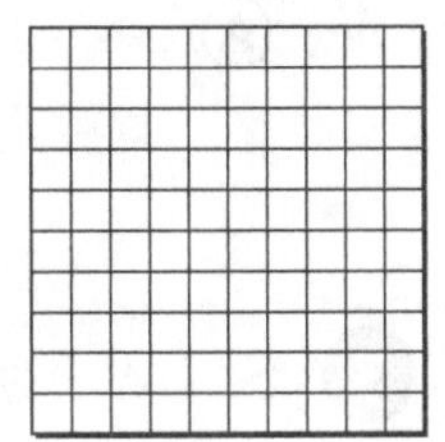

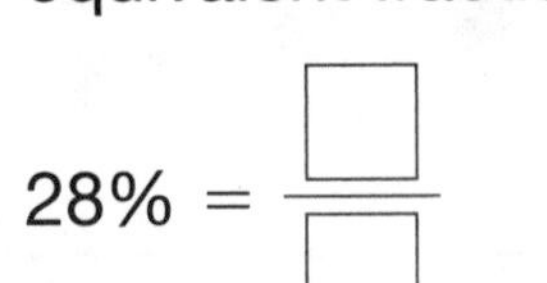

$28\% = \frac{\square}{\square}$

8 What would you tell Mark if he asked which percent is equivalent to $\frac{9}{25}$?

Ⓐ 9% Ⓑ 18% Ⓒ 25% Ⓓ 36%

9 Carl said that he knows how to multiply 4×265 using the Distributive Property. Show how Carl solves this problem.

$\mathbf{4 \times 265} =$

10 Maggie knows how to use the Associative Property to multiply. What is Maggie's answer?

$(8 \times 8) \times 20$

Ⓐ 64 Ⓑ 128 Ⓒ 160 Ⓓ 1,280

11 Use the counters to solve.

$12 + w + 7 = 25$

12 Use algebra to solve.

$m \div 6 = 18$

Ⓐ $m = 108$ Ⓑ $m = 24$ Ⓒ $m = 12$ Ⓓ $m = 3$

13 Find the perimeter and area of the board.

115 ft

8 ft

Perimeter = ☐ + ☐ + ☐ + ☐ = ☐ **ft**

Area = ☐ × ☐ = ☐ **sq ft**

14 Find the perimeter and the area.

98 ft

21 ft

$P = 2(\ell + w) = 2(\square + \square) = 2(\square) = \square$ **ft**

$A = \ell \times w = \square \times \square = \square$ **sq ft**

15 On the coordinate grid, draw the points of these coordinate pairs. Label each point.

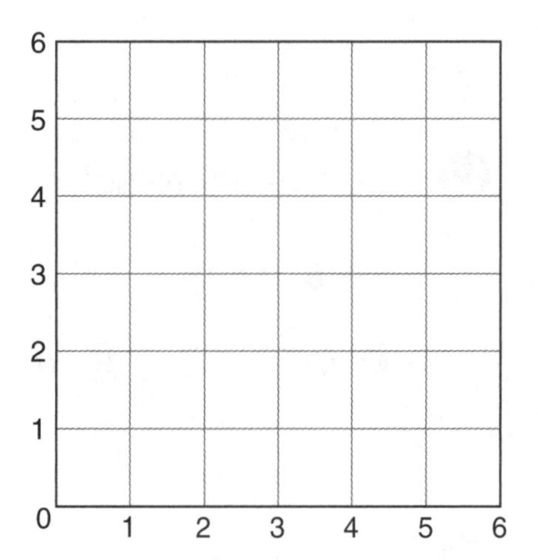

Point A (1, 3)

Point B (2, 5)

Point C (3, 3)

Point D (2, 1)

Connect the points in order. What are the coordinates of the point in the center of the figure you drew? ____________

16 Use the scale drawing and a centimeter ruler to answer the question.

About how tall are the actual Lower Falls of the Yellowstone River?

____________ **m**

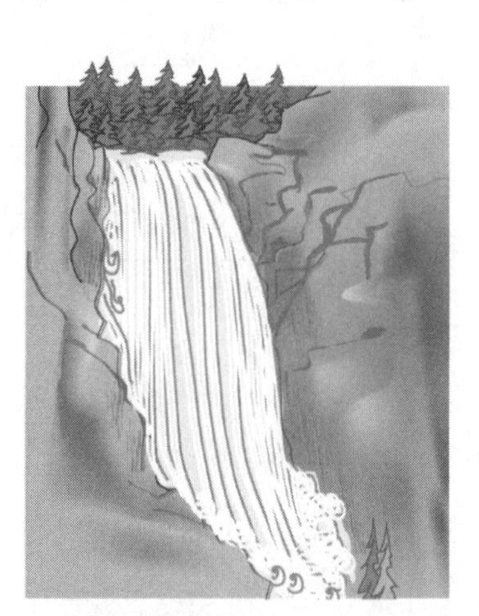

Lower Falls of the Yellowstone River
Scale: 2 cm = 40 m

17 Use the circle graph to answer the question.

Which sections of the graph use about the same amount of water as washing?

____

____

June Water Use

Washing

Watering Plants

Leaky Faucets

Showering

Toilets

18 Use the bar graph to answer the question.

About how many times more water is used for washing than is used for watering plants in July?

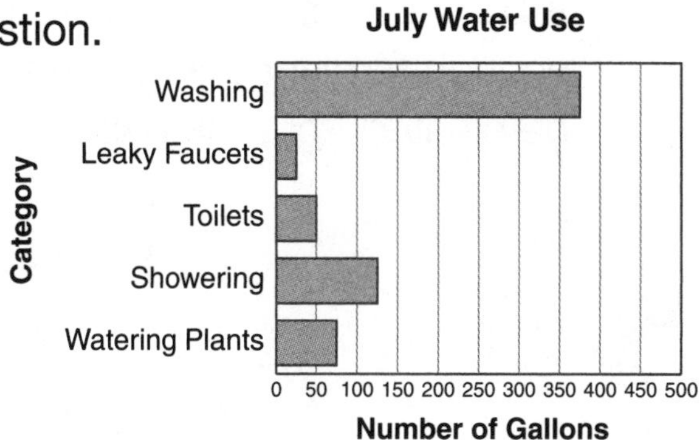

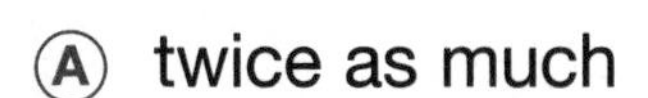

Ⓐ twice as much

Ⓑ three times as much

Ⓒ four times as much

Ⓓ five times as much

19 Use the line graph to answer the question.

What pattern do you see in the data overall?

____

____

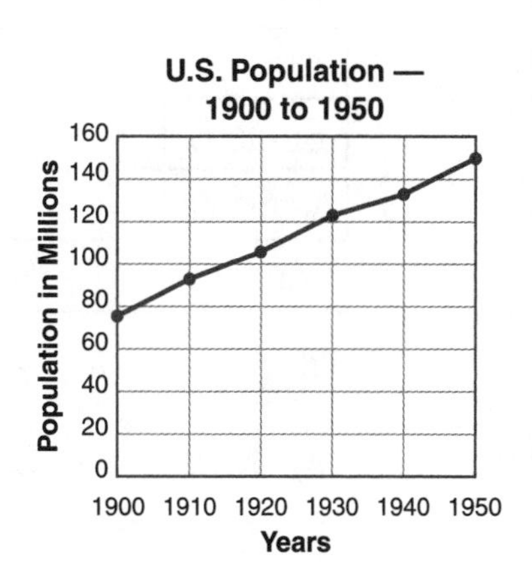

20 Use logical reasoning to solve the problem.

A bag contains 240 flower bulbs. Each group of 20 bulbs is enough to plant 1 garden plot. How many garden plots could be planted from the bag?

______ garden plots could be planted from 240 bulbs.

21 Use equivalent fractions to solve the problem.

A bag contains 900 flower bulbs. Each group of 25 bulbs is enough to plant one garden plot. How many garden plots could be planted from the bag?

$\frac{1}{25} = \frac{x}{900}$

$x = \square$

22 Use the table to answer the question.

Favorite Movies	
Type	**Number of Votes**
Musical	12
Horror	11
Comedy	14
Animated	12
Action	16

What are the mean and the median of the data?

Ⓐ Mean: 12, Median: 12

Ⓑ Mean: 12, Median: 13

Ⓒ Mean: 13, Median: 12

Ⓓ Mean: 13, Median: 14

23 Solve by making a list.

A male and a female fox produced 6 offspring. Two of their offspring are females. One daughter had 3 offspring. One of her babies is female. How many males and females were in this family, counting the parents?

There were ____ males and ____ females in this family.

24 Solve by using a chart.

Carly's cats always had two more male than female kittens in their litter. The first litter had 5 males. The next litter had 4 males. The third litter had 6 males. How many kittens were in the 3 litters in all?

	Females (M–2)	Males (M)	Total
Litter 1			
Litter 2			
Litter 3			

____ + ____ + ____ = ____

There were ____ kittens in all.

25 Solve using a table.

On the first day of a fossil dig, 8 students were digging at Site A. Five more students than this were at Site B.

On Day 2, the number of students at Site A tripled and the number at Site B was doubled from the day before.

The total number of students who worked at Site A was 10 less than the total number that worked at Site B. The total number of students who worked at Site B was 55.

How many students worked at each site on the third day?

	Day 1	Day 2	Day 3	Total
Site A				
Site B				

The total number of students who worked at Site A on Day 3 was ____.

The total number of students who worked at Site B on Day 3 was ____.

26 Solve using logic.

The first day of an excavation, scientists digging for fossils found half as many fossils at Site A as at Site B. They found 18 fossils at Site B. The second day they found 4 fewer fossils at each site than they found the day before. The third day they found the same number at each site. They found 22 fossils in all on the third day. How many fossils did they find at each site in all?

Scientists found ____ fossils at Site A in all.

Scientists found ____fossils at Site B in all.

GLOSSARY

A

algebraic equation A number sentence with a variable and at least one operational symbol.

area The number of square units needed to cover a two-dimensional figure.

Associative Property of Addition When adding, the way in which addends are grouped does not change the sum.
$(a + b) + c = a + (b + c)$

Associative Property of Multiplication When multiplying, the way in which factors are grouped does not change the product.
$a \times (b \times c) = (a \times b) \times c$

B

bar graph A graph that uses bars shaped like rectangles to show and compare data.

bones The structures in your body that support weight and make marrow.

C

cave A hollow area beneath the earth's surface.

circle graph A graph that uses the parts of a circle to show and compare data.

Commutative Property of Addition Numbers can be added in any order.
$a + b = b + a$

Commutative Property of Multiplication Numbers can be multiplied in any order.
$a \times b = b \times a$

coordinate grid A grid that can be formed by two number axes: a horizontal axis that goes left and right and a vertical axis that goes up and down.

coordinate pair Two numbers that identify the location of a point on a coordinate grid.

D

data A group of names, numbers, or other information that is related. Data is often put in tables or graphs.

decimal A number with one or more digits to the right of a decimal point.

den The shelter or home of a wild animal.

denominator The number below the line in a fraction. It tells the total number of equal parts in the whole or group.

Distributive Property When two addends are multiplied by a factor, the product is the same as if each addend was multiplied by the factor and those products were added.
$a \times (b + c) = (a \times b) + (a \times c)$

E

equation A statement that two mathematical expressions are equal.

equivalent fractions Fractions that name the same number. $\frac{1}{2}$ and $\frac{3}{6}$ are equivalent fractions.

event A possible outcome in probability.

F

formula An equation that states a relationship among quantities.

fraction A number that stands for part of a whole, a part of a collection, or a part of a region.

G

geologist A person who studies the structure of the earth.

graph A drawing or picture that shows data in an organized way.

H

hundredth(s) One or more parts out of 100 equal parts.

I

invertebrates Animals without backbones.

L

line graph A graph in which connected line segments show the changes in data over time.

litter The young produced at one birth by mammals.

M

mammals A class of vertebrates with self-regulating body temperature and hair.

marrow The substance inside bones that produces blood cells.

mollusks Any of various members of mostly marine invertebrates, including oysters and clams.

N

number line A line that is numbered along equally spaced marks.

number sentence An equation with numbers.

numerator The number above the line in a fraction that tells the portion of the equal parts in the whole or the group.

O

origin The location of the coordinate pair (0, 0) on a coordinate grid.

P

percent The number of parts out of 100. It uses the symbol %.

perimeter The distance around a figure.

place value The amount or value of a position in a number.

population The total number of people in a specified area.

probability A number from 0 to 1 that tells the likelihood that an event will occur.

proportions Equations showing that two ratios are equal.

R

ratio A comparison of two numbers by division.

S

scale A ratio between two sets of measurements.

scale drawing A drawing that is created using a scale.

shrews Tiny mouse-like animals that burrow in the ground.

T

table A listing of data in rows and columns.

tenth(s) One or more parts out of 10 equal parts.

V

variable A letter used to represent a numerical value.

vertebrates Animals with backbones.